ALAN H

C000178944

*it's so*

# NATURAL

Angus&Robertson
An imprint of HarperCollins*Publishers*

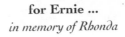

for Ernie ...
*in memory of Rhonda*

**Angus&Robertson**
An imprint of the HarperCollins*Publishers,* Australia

First published in Australia in 1993
Reprinted in 1994 (twice)
Angus&Robertson edition 1995
HarperCollins*Publishers* Pty Limited
ACN 009 913 517
A member of the HarperCollins*Publishers* (Australia) Pty Limited Group

**HarperCollins*Publishers***
25 Ryde Road, Pymble, Sydney, NSW 2073, Australia
31 View Road, Glenfield, Auckland 10, New Zealand
77-85 Fulham Palace Road, London W6 8JB, United Kingdom
Hazelton Lanes, 55 Avenue Road, Suite 2900, Toronto, Ontario M5R 3L2
*and* 1995 Markham Road, Scarborough, Ontario M1B 5M8, Canada
10 East 53rd Street, New York NY 10032, USA

National Library of Australia Cataloguing-in-Publication data:

Hayes, Alan B. (Alan Bruce), 1949– .
It's so natural: hints from A to Z.
ISBN 0 207 18989 7.
1. Home economics. 2. Herbs. I. Title.
640.41

Cover illustration and design Kate Mitchell
Printed in Australia by The Griffin Press, Adelaide

9 8 7 6 5 4   95 96 97 98

## FOREWORD

*It's So Natural* is a compilation of the weekly newspaper column I write of the same name, published in newspapers throughout Australia. Read by thousands of people each week in every state, the information deals with environmentally safe advice and solutions, especially easy-to-make natural products within the home.

It includes the versatility of herbs in and around the home: health, garden and household pests, cleaners, pet care, cosmetics, and many other products and applications that are just as effective as chemicals.

I have gathered and practised these ideas over the years, inventing them in response to my and others' needs. Other ideas have passed down through my family generations and are sound herbal lore.

My zealousness for a natural lifestyle has quite often met with the label of eccentricity. Nowadays this lifestyle is much more acceptable and widely practised.

Living in harmony with our environment will guarantee future generations the same joy and beauty we have been able to experience. Let us encourage all those around us to be more responsible, because it will make a difference in the long run.

Alan B. Hayes

## GENERAL ADVICE
### Allergic Reactions

Because of the increase in skin sensitivities and allergic reactions, it is important to test any new substance or ingredient before use. This can be done by a simple patch test. Do this by placing a small amount of the substance on the tender skin of your arm and covering it with a bandage for approximately 24 hours. If your skin reacts and reddens, itches or blisters, immediately remove the test patch and do not use that product or ingredient.

If your skin reacts to a cosmetic product that contains glycerine or anhydrous lanolin *(wool fat)* in the recipe, substitute completely with beeswax. This will not affect the beneficial properties.

Some vegetable oils and essential oils can irritate sensitive skins, particularly on the face and around the neck. Those which may cause allergic reactions are:

| | |
|---|---|
| almond oil | parsley *(large doses only)* |
| bay leaf oil | peppermint |
| bergamot | rosemary *(hypersensitive people only)* |
| geranium *(all types)* | sage |
| lavender *(very large doses)* | spearmint |
| neroli | thyme |

Herbs which may cause allergic reactions are:

| | |
|---|---|
| lime *(linden)* blossom | pennyroyal |
| lovage | violet leaves |
| nettles | |

Other ingredients:

| | |
|---|---|
| cocoa butter | glycerine |
| anhydrous lanolin | |

## ESSENTIAL OILS
### WARNING

Pure essential oils are used in many of the recipes in this book. Used as directed they are perfectly safe. If accidentally swallowed, however, they can cause poisoning, and therefore they should be kept tightly sealed in the bottles they came in and *out of the reach of children.*

## ACHES AND PAINS

Cold, rheumatic pain responds to the astringent qualities of a ginger bath. Add 15 grams of crushed ginger or 1 teaspoon of powdered ginger while the taps are running. Do not use more as it can burn and irritate the skin. Ginger is not recommended for people who have skin problems.

Cabbage leaves will ease hot, painful joints. Simply bind clean, slightly bruised leaves firmly into position around the joint with a roll-on bandage. Leave on overnight.

*See also Chamomile, Essential Oils, Pain, Garlic, Itching, Arthritis.*

## ACNE

Occasional pimples are a nuisance, unsightly, and always appear when you least want them to. The following remedy is quick and easy, and will heal a pimple overnight.

Bruise a fresh marigold (Calendula officinalis) petal and then gently, but firmly, press it onto the affected spot for 2 to 3 minutes. Repeat this application from time to time.

In the morning there will be just a trace of redness. This will completely disappear in a few hours if the procedure is repeated one more time.

If a fresh marigold petal is not available, use a fresh leaf in the same way.

### Herbal Compress

Help to keep your skin clear by applying a herbal compress to troubled areas. It is an easy and efficient way of treating spots and blemishes with a generous quantity of herbal infusion.

*2 teaspoons dried lemon balm*
*2 teaspoons dried chamomile*
*2 teaspoons dried marigold petals*

Put all the ingredients in a ceramic bowl and add 2½ cups (600 ml) of boiling water. Cover and steep overnight, then strain through fine muslin. Store in an airtight bottle in the refrigerator for up to 7 days.

Prior to use, heat on the stove until lukewarm. To make the compress, dip sterile gauze or cottonwool into the warm infusion and hold it against the affected area of skin for 15 minutes. Do not use it near your eyes, or on very reddened skin. This compress can be diluted with boiled water if necessary.

## AFTERSHAVE

### Herbal Aftershave

*1 ½ tablespoons chopped fresh sage leaves*
*1 ½ tablespoons fresh rosemary leaves*
*1 ½ cups (375 ml) cider vinegar*
*1 ½ cups (375 ml) witch-hazel (from the chemist)*

Put the herbs in a wide-mouthed glass jar and add gently warmed vinegar. Seal the jar airtight and place where it will receive plenty of hot sunlight for 2 weeks. Strain through muslin, mix with the witch-hazel and drip through filter paper.

Store in an airtight glass bottle.

Pat onto skin with a piece of cottonwool.

## AIR FRESHENERS

The refreshing and aromatic properties of herbs and flowers can be used in many different ways to keep your home fragrantly fresh, and remove stale and other unwanted odours.

None of these sprays should be sprayed directly onto children, pets or furniture. Hands should be washed if you have touched the oils, as oils can sting your eyes.

### Antiseptic Spray

Use this to eliminate bathroom odours, freshen a sickroom, or anywhere else that an antiseptic spray is needed. Choose from any of the following herb oils, listed in descending order of their antiseptic powers: thyme, orange flower, bergamot, juniper, clove, lavender, neroli, peppermint, rosemary, sandalwood and eucalyptus.

*24 to 30 drops chosen oil*
*1 teaspoon vodka or methylated spirits*
*2 cups (500 ml) distilled water*

Dissolve the oil in the alcohol, add to the distilled water and store in a pump-spray bottle. Shake well to mix and use on a fine mist setting.

## Antifungal and Antibacterial Spray
The following air freshener spray has natural antifungal and antibacterial properties, and is long-lasting.

*25 drops lavender oil*
*10 drops lemon oil*
*5 drops eucalyptus oil*
*1 teaspoon methylated spirits*
*2 cups (500 ml) distilled water*

Dissolve the essential oils in the methylated spirits and add this to a pump-spray bottle that contains 2 cups (500 ml) of water. Shake well to mix, and use as required.

## Bathroom Spray
The following herbal air freshener will keep your toilet and bathroom smelling fragrant and fresh.

*4 teaspoons dried lavender or hyssop*
*1 tablespoon vodka*
*2 ½ cups (600 ml) distilled water*

Place the herbs in a ceramic bowl, bring the distilled water to the boil in an enamel or stainless steel pan and pour over the herbs. Cover, infuse overnight, then strain through very fine muslin, squeezing all liquid from the herbs. Add the vodka, drip through filter paper and store in a pump-spray bottle.

## Bacteria Buster
This air freshener spray is the one most commonly used in my own household. Its blend of oils gives it a delightful aroma, releasing an immediate burst to tease the senses and then a lingering, elusive scent to keep bathrooms and other rooms smelling fragrant and fresh.

It combats airborne bacteria making it an excellent choice when winter colds and 'flu are prevalent. It also has antifungal properties.

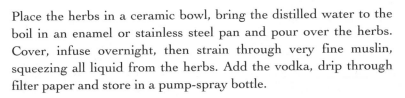

*0.4 ml chamomile oil*
*0.2 ml lavender oil*
*0.2 ml ylang ylang*
*0.4 ml jasmine oil*
*1.5 ml bergamot oil*
*1 ml nutmeg*
*2 teaspoons methylated spirits*
*2 cups (500 ml) distilled water*

Dissolve all the oils in the alcohol and add to a pump-spray bottle that contains the water. Shake well to mix and use on a fine mist setting as required.

## FRAGRANT OILS

Pure essential oils can be used in many different ways to perfume a room, remove unwanted odours and provide protection against bacteria and airborne fungi.

• Add a few drops of fragrant oil to a shallow dish of warm water set on a sunny windowsill or radiator. As the oil evaporates, its aroma will fill the room.

• For a sickroom or bathroom, moisten a sponge with boiling water and add a few drops of essential oil. Place the sponge in a dish and moisten it with boiling water twice a day, refreshing it with a few drops of oil twice a week. Use lavender or peppermint oil in a sickroom as protection against bacteria.

• One or two drops of oil on a warm light bulb will quickly fill a room with its fragrance. Do not use oils containing alcohol. Burning pure essential oils will kill airborne bacteria and fungi. Try thyme, lavender, pine or eucalyptus for their fresh fragrance.

• A few drops of oil in the vacuum cleaner bag leaves a delightful fragrance as you clean.

• For a sweet-smelling bathroom, pour a few drops of your favourite essential oil onto the spout of the hot tap and turn it on for a few moments to release the fragrance. The delightful aroma will fill the room for some time.

*See also Carpets, Essential Oils, Lemon, Kitchen, Paint (Odour), Pomander, Xmas (House Spray).*

# ALOE VERA (*ALOE BARBADENSIS*)

## THE HEALING HERB

Of aloe vera's many uses, most probably the best known is in the treatment of burns. Its triple action of pain relief and antiseptic and healing qualities makes this remedy suitable for even serious burns and scalds.

It contains allantoin, protein, minerals, vitamins A, B1, B2, C, E and K, and 18 amino acids, all of which give it unique properties. It is available from health food stores as a liquid extract or gel.

Varicose ulcers will respond to daily applications of aloe vera gel, and when spread on the cleaned ulcers it will encourage rapid healing.

As a hair preparation, it is unequalled. Use it for greasy scalp conditions, dandruff and as a general hair conditioner, and there will soon be a noticeable improvement. Use as a liquid extract or gel, homemade or bought — include it in shampoo or massage it directly into the scalp.

The liquid extract can be used as a mouth rinse, or the gel can be rubbed into the gums, as it is also good for bad breath. Alternatively, brush your teeth and gums with the gel once a week as a precautionary measure.

Various skin conditions, apart from burns, will also respond well to aloe vera gel treatment. Tinea ('Athlete's foot') and other fungal infections, and infections of the fingers and toe-nails should have twice-daily applications of the gel. Superficial cuts, scratches, abrasions, stings and bites will heal with the same treatment.

Aloe vera is easily grown in the home garden, and can be purchased ready to plant out from most nurseries. However, make sure that the plant you purchase is Aloe barbadenis, since there are many other varieties which don't have the same healing properties.

*Did you know ...*

that aloe vera is one of the oldest medicinal plants in history? And that ancient Assyrians, Babylonians, Egyptians and Jews endowed this remarkable plant with holy virtues? For centuries it has been surrounded by folklore about its wide range of benefits and healing powers, and known deservedly as the 'holy herb'.

# ANTISEPTIC

A few drops of lavender or tea tree oil in a cup of water makes an all-purpose antiseptic for cuts, scratches and other abrasions.

Alternatively, blend equal parts of eucalyptus oil and aloe vera juice and store in an amber-coloured glass bottle until needed. Best used for grazes and scratches. Keep no longer than 2 months.

Apply either antiseptic with clean lint or cottonwool.

*See also Air Fresheners, Disinfectant.*

# ANTS

Most households suffer from ant invasion at some time, especially in dry weather. If they really bother you, hunt down their nest and destroy it, but only as a last resort. Try to discourage them from staying in or entering your house instead.

• Sprinkle a combination of bicarbonate of soda and black pepper wherever they gather. They can't stand it and will soon vanish. Sage sprinkled in cupboards is also an effective deterrent.
• Rub a cut lemon on and around your sink. Strewing slices of lemon in their paths is said to deter ants if they can't find an easy way around them.
• Keep food scraps and crumbs off ant-accessible areas, and leave repellents or baits on ant trails.
• Bone meal sprinkled around the outside walls of the house and throughout the garden will drive ants away.

## SUGAR BAIT

Dissolve 3 tablespoons of sugar in 1 cup (250 ml) of warm water, allow to cool, then stir in 1 tablespoon of bicarbonate of soda. Store in a bottle in the refrigerator until needed.

Put bottle capfuls on ant nests and trails — anywhere ants gather, including the inside of the house — and cover if wet. This type of bait works on the insect's body heat. As they feed on it the body warmth makes them explode.

## BORAX BAIT

This bait is particularly suitable for indoor use. Mix 2 cups (500 g) of sugar and 2 tablespoons of borax together, then dissolve the mixture in 1 cup (250 ml) of water. Pour into glass jars loosely filled with cottonwool. Punch holes in the lid and locate wherever you find ants.

## DESTROYING THE NEST

If you feel that you must destroy the nest, try pouring boiling water, mixed with a little detergent, down it. Repeat this every few days until the nest is evacuated.

A kerosene oil emulsion is also effective. Mix together 2 cups (500 ml) of water, ¼ cup (60 ml) of kerosene, ¼ cup (60 ml) of liquid detergent and 2 tablespoons of sunflower oil. Pour down ant nest holes to destroy them or spray on emerging ants.

Both these methods may have to be repeated several times to have the desired result. You can also combine both methods for greater effectiveness, and place baits around for emerging ants.

## ANT BITES

If you are bitten by ants and there is bracken nearby, rub the juice of a bracken stem on the bite as quickly as possible. It will prevent the resultant painful swellings.

## APHIDS

An effective natural spray for controlling aphids and scale can be made from soap and washing soda.

### Soap Spray

*100 g grated soap*
*260 g washing soda*
*14 litres water*

Boil a small amount of the water, reserving the remainder. Stir in the washing soda until it is completely dissolved and add the grated soap. Heat the mixture, at the same time stirring the soap until it has dissolved. Add the remaining water, agitate the mixture and spray as required.

Use to control sucking pests, particularly on citrus trees.

## ARTHRITIS

Arthritic joints are very painful and often stubborn in responding to treatments. It is important to maintain a simple diet and avoid sugar, tea, margarine, nuts, vinegar, soft drinks and ice-cream. Fruit juice may be drunk, but only sparingly, and should be taken by the spoonful so that it will assimilate with saliva.

Painful joints can be relieved by massaging garlic ointment into the affected areas.

*See also Garlic.*

## BAD BREATH

*See Aloe Vera, Herbs (Green Herbal Drink), Pets (Bad Breath).*

## BALLPOINT INK

To remove ballpoint ink from clothing, rub the affected area with methylated spirits, then wash the garment.

## BASIL

*Did you know ...*

that in times of yesteryear the herb basil was used to test a young girl's virginity? A girl under suspicion of being unchaste was required to walk through a swarm of bees holding a bunch of basil in her hands. If the bees let her alone she was still pure.

## BATH

### AROMATIC BATH

Soothe depressing moods with a fragrant bath using the following essential oils.

**Melancholy:** rose, neroli or chamomile
**Anxiety:** chamomile, neroli or lavender
**Anger:** rose or chamomile

Dilute 30 drops of your chosen oil with 2 tablespoons of olive oil, and add 10 drops of this mixture to the bath while the taps are running. For maximum effect, close windows and door.

Keep leftover oil in an amber glass bottle with a tight-fitting lid, but no longer than 2 months.

*See also Insomnia, Juniper, Stress, Ylang Ylang.*

### THERAPEUTIC BATH

A therapeutic bath can do wonders in speeding up recovery when suffering from a cold, a stuffed-up nose and aching muscles and joints. For maximum effect close all windows and the bathroom door.

If you are nauseated or running a fever, it is advisable not to take a full bath; instead sponge off underarms and genitals.

## Bath Oil

*6 drops pine oil*
*6 drops eucalyptus oil*
*6 drops cypress oil*

Run water as hot as you can stand it, and when almost full add the essential oils.

Sit with your knees up and your head between them so that you can fully inhale the restorative vapours. As the water cools slosh it all over your body.

Get out, vigorously dry yourself with a warm towel and then wrap yourself in another warm towel for a few minutes. To finish off, try this oil rub.

## After-bath Rub

*½ cup (125 ml) almond oil*
*2 drops eucalyptus oil*
*3 drops lavender oil*
*2 drops thyme oil*

Combine the oils together and, after your bath, rub your entire body with it.

*See also First Aid, Colds and Flu, Itching.*

### SACHETS

These can be made with dried flowers of English lavender.

Put a small pile of lavender in the middle of a small square of fabric, such as lavender-coloured, sprigged, thin cotton and tie into a ball.

The fabric should be closely-woven so that the lavender can be kept inside the sachet. Secure the sachet with a long piece of string or ribbon.

Tie several of these sachet-bags together with a lavender-coloured bow and attach an appropriate swing tag for a very special gift.

To use, tie a sachet to the hot tap and run hot water over it to release the natural essences. It may be used 2 or 3 times before its essences are used up.

*See also Yarrow, Ylang Ylang.*

# BATHROOM

## CLEANING

• Bath and basin stains can be removed with a paste of borax and lemon juice.

• For a mild abrasive to clean baths, sinks, toilet bowl and tiles, make a light paste of bicarbonate of soda and water.

• Bathroom and kitchen ceramic tiles can be wiped over with eucalyptus disinfectant liquid. Dissolve 12 drops of eucalyptus oil in 10 ml of methylated spirits and add to 8 cups (2 litres) of tepid water (this aids dispersal of the oil).

• To whiten the blackened grout between tiles apply a paste of bicarbonate of soda with a soft toothbrush. This mixture can also be used to remove mould.

• To clean shower screens use Lavender Glass Cleaner. *See Windows.*

• Shower curtains can be cleaned by scrubbing with white vinegar.

• Mould and mildew can be removed from bathroom surfaces by applying white vinegar. Leave on overnight before scrubbing off and wiping clean.

• Clean the inside of non-septic toilet bowls with a paste of borax and lemon juice. For septic systems use white vinegar, since it won't harm the microbes that break down the sewage in the tank.

• To sanitise your toilet and leave it smelling fresh, pour some white vinegar into it and leave overnight.

## All-purpose Cleanser

This natural cleanser can be used to clean and disinfect toilets, bathrooms, kitchen benches and sinks.

*4 tablespoons dried soapwort*
*8 cups (2 litres) white vinegar*
*2 tablespoons dried thyme*
*1 tablespoon eucalyptus oil*
*washing soda*

Put the soapwort and thyme in a large, wide-mouthed glass jar. Gently warm the vinegar, pour into the jar, seal tightly and leave where it will receive plenty of hot sunlight for 2 weeks. Shake the jar well every day to agitate the contents. Strain the vinegar and store in a tightly-capped bottle.

To use, mix sufficient washing soda with the herbal vinegar to form a paste.

*See also Taps, Tiles.*

## Bathroom Mould Spray

This solution will remove surface mould from bathroom tiles and painted bathroom walls, and also acts as a natural disinfectant.

*1 tablespoon (20 ml) eucalyptus oil*
*1 tablespoon (20 ml) methylated spirits*
*2 cups (500 ml) water*

Dissolve the oil in the alcohol and add to a pump-spray bottle containing the water. Spray over affected area, a small section at a time, and wipe off. For stubborn mould, use a little 'elbow grease'.

*See also Air Fresheners.*

## BEE STINGS

*See First Aid.*

## BICARBONATE OF SODA

Supermarket shelves are filled with household cleaners containing strong chemicals which can pollute the environment and pose health hazards. Yet there is an alternative: safe, simple bicarbonate of soda — an inexpensive and effective general-purpose cleaner.

So next time you clean, try 'humble' bicarbonate of soda.

• Drains can be unblocked by dissolving bicarbonate of soda in boiling water. To clear kitchen drains that are blocked with fat, pour down a cup each of bicarbonate of soda and salt, followed by two jugs of boiling water.
• For dirty saucepans that don't respond to steel wool, add cold water and 2 teaspoons of bicarbonate of soda to the pot and bring to the boil. When cool, clean off with steel wool. Tannin stains in cups and teapots can be removed by rubbing with a damp cloth and bicarbonate of soda.
• Use as a mild alkali for neutralising acid stains. Soak stained fabric in warm water containing two teaspoons of bicarbonate of soda, leave for an hour, then rinse well.

• Grease can be removed by pouring hot water on stains and covering with dry bicarbonate of soda.

*See also Bathroom, Carpets (Deodorising), Iron, Kitchen, Laminex, Laundry (Soiled Nappies), Oven, Silverware, Taps, Tiles.*

## BIRDS

*See Garden.*

## BLOOD STAINS

To remove blood stains from clothing, soak immediately in cold salted water for at least 30 minutes.

Mix cornmeal with water and rub onto the stain. Allow to dry, then brush away and wash as normal.

## BOOKS

*See Silverfish.*

## BRACKEN

*See Ants, Ticks.*

## BRASS

Clean with half a lemon dipped in salt, or a mixture of vinegar and salt made into a fine paste. Finish off by a good rubbing with a soft cloth.

Lacquered brass should be wiped over with a damp cloth or sponge.

Lamp bases, fire tools and surrounds can be cleaned by rubbing in one direction only with fine dry steel wool. Circular motions will scratch the metal.

## BRICKS

Stains can be removed from unsealed bricks by applying white vinegar. Brush over with a stiff brush dipped in vinegar until the stain disappears.

To bring them up to a beautiful shine apply the following polish:

## Brick Polish

*½ cup (125 ml) lemon juice*
*1 cup (250 ml) olive oil*
*2½ ml eucalyptus oil*
*2½ ml natural turpentine*

Thoroughly mix all ingredients and store in a tightly sealed bottle.
Label clearly.

Ideal for internal brick feature walls.


## BRUISE OIL

This is an old-fashioned recipe passed down to me by my
grandmother, and was the oily concoction given when
I played football as a teenager.

### Herbal Bruise Oil

1 handful of each of the following herbs:

| | |
|---|---|
| *lemon balm* | *sage* |
| *rosemary* | *lavender flowers* |
| *chamomile flowers* | *southernwood* |
| *rosebuds* | *wood betony* |
| *feverfew* | *wormwood* |

Chop the herbs up into small pieces and pack them into a
large, wide-mouth glass jar. Add sufficient olive oil to cover them,
seal the jar and stand in a sunny spot for 2 weeks. Shake the
contents of the jar every day.

Put the contents in an enamel or stainless steel pan and gently
boil until the herbs are crisp. Remove from heat and strain
through fine muslin, squeezing all the oil from the herbs.

Store in a tightly sealed, amber-coloured glass bottle, and use as
needed.


## BURNS

*See Aloe Vera, First Aid, Pets (Burns).*


## BUTTER SUBSTITUTES

*See Dietary Substitutes.*

# CANDLES

*See Insect Repellents.*

# CANS

*See Recycling.*

# CAR FRESHENER

A few drops of essential oil sprinkled on a tissue and placed in the air vent of your car will keep it fragrant and fresh as you drive. Do not put this on the heater, as it could be a flame risk.

Citrus oils will refresh stale air and basil and peppermint will help you to remain alert while driving. (However, if you are very tired make sure you stop for a rest.)

# CAR RADIATOR

To clean the car radiator: drain the cooling system and flush it out with running water. Close drain outlets, add 200 g washing soda to the radiator, fill with clean water, and run the car for short distances only for 3 days. Drain the washing soda water from the system, flush thoroughly, and fill with clean water.

Do not use this method if your car has an aluminium head or the cooling system is in poor condition.

# CARPETS

## GREASE AND OIL STAINS

Without realising that the soles of my shoes were covered with oil and grease, I left a tell-tale track of greasy footprints all over our woollen carpet. I was adamantly told to remove the stains, or suffer dire consequences.

To remove oil and grease stains, mix sufficient water and kaolin (china clay — available from the chemist) to form a thick paste, and then spread this over the soiled areas. Leave the paste until it is completely dry (24 to 36 hours). Reduce to a powder with a stiff broom, and then vacuum up.

Oil and grease stains are completely removed this way.

You can substitute fuller's earth for the kaolin, and use the mixture to successfully dry clean natural fibre carpets, following the same procedure.

## STAIN REMOVER

A general, all-purpose stain remover, for all carpets, can be made by dissolving half a cup of pure soap flakes or grated soap in boiling water. Allow to cool, then whip until stiff.

Apply to a small area at a time, allow to dry, then remove the residue and wipe with a damp cloth. When the carpet is almost dry, brush up the pile.

*See also Ink Stains.*

## Carpet Shampoo

This can be used to lightly shampoo carpets or to spot-clean.

*4 tablespoons dried soapwort*
*distilled water*

Place soapwort in an enamel or stainless steel pan and add enough water to cover. Boil for 5 minutes, cool, and strain through muslin.

Use neat for spot-cleaning or dilute 2 to 1 by volume, or more if needed, for shampooing.

## DEODORISING

To deodorise carpets, sprinkle bicarbonate of soda over them, leave for an hour or two, then vacuum off.

To leave your carpets smelling fragrant and fresh, mix some of your favourite aromatic oil, a drop at a time, with the bicarbonate of soda.

Add a few drops of the same oil to the vacuum cleaner bag to leave a delightful, aromatic fragrance as you clean.

## CHAMOMILE (*MATRICARIA RECUTICA*)

'German Chamomile'

A low growing, self-seeding annual with yellow and white daisy-like flowers that are used to make the popular tea. The essential oil added to the bath has slightly antiseptic effects and is particularly beneficial to people with oily skin. Regular bathing helps to reduce and smooth out wrinkles, tone up relaxed muscles, and is very relaxing and soothing, thereby calming the nerves and promoting sound, natural sleep. An infusion is ideal as a steam bath to cleanse and soothe the face, and is especially suitable for people with sensitive and delicate skin.

Taken as an inhalation, chamomile will help to soothe an overactive and tired brain, and if you drink it as a tea prior to going to bed it will help to ensure a restful sleep. Add an infusion or oil to your herbal shampoos, or use it as a hair rinse, to brighten fair hair. The oil makes an excellent scalp massage for unhealthy, lifeless hair.

Taken whenever needed, chamomile tea is without doubt one of the safest and gentlest of all natural medicines. It may be used for the following:

- to calm the nerves
- to soothe cramp or colic in the bowels *(see Gripe Water for Infants)*
- to help in the treatment of red, inflamed eyes (add the cold tea to an eye-glass and bathe)
- to expel worms
- to prevent migraine headaches
- for menstrual pain
- nervous tension

Chamomile tea bags are readily available from all good health food stores and some supermarkets.

## CHAMOMILE ESSENCE

Chamomile essence has a low toxicity and so is especially suitable for children. It will soothe skin disorders such as acne, burns, stings, and rashes, and is excellent for conjunctivitis, infants' teething problems, rheumatism and neuralgia. General aches and pains, headache and earache will often respond to chamomile.

- For rheumatism and other aches and pains, massage the body with 25 ml of soya oil to which has been added 2 drops each of chamomile oil and rosemary oil.
- Skin irritations can be soothed by dabbing with cottonwool soaked in a lotion made by combining 5 tablespoons of olive oil, 10 drops chamomile oil and 5 drops of Borneo camphor.

• Migraine headaches can sometimes be helped by sucking a lump of sugar which has been soaked in four drops of chamomile oil.

## Chamomile Oatmeal Scrub

This gentle facial scrub can be used to thoroughly cleanse oily skin and leave it glowing. Make as required.

*2 teaspoons dried chamomile flowers*
*1¼ cups (300 ml) boiling water*
*⅔ cup (90 g) oatmeal*
*3 tablespoons warm milk*

Put the chamomile in a ceramic bowl, add the boiling water, cover and allow to infuse overnight. Strain through very fine muslin, squeezing all liquid from the herbs.

Grind the oatmeal to a fine powder and mix this with 1 tablespoon of chamomile infusion and the warm milk, to make a paste.

Gently rub over the face, avoiding the eyes, then rinse off with warm water. Gently pat dry with a soft towel.

*See also First Aid (Sedative), Fungicide, Teas (Herbal).*

## CHEESE SUBSTITUTE

*See Dietary Substitutes.*

## CHEST RUB

*See Colds and Flu.*

## CHINA CEMENT

Broken china and other ceramic objects can be readily repaired with the following glue.

Dissolve sufficient gum arabic (available from art suppliers) in warm water to make a thick solution. Stir in the plaster of Paris until quite thick, then apply with a brush to the broken edges and press them together.

This cement is white and can be coloured by the addition of different earth oxides, such as red iron, black iron, yellow ochre, cobalt, chrome, burnt umber, etc. They can be mixed with a little water and blended together to achieve different colours and shades prior to mixing with the glue.

Oxide pigments are available from hardware stores and ceramic suppliers.

## CHRISTMAS

*See Xmas.*

## CITRUS TREES

*See Garden (Feeding Citrus Trees).*

## CLEANING

Once, all household cleaners were made at home using whatever natural ingredients were close at hand. Timber furniture was rubbed with lemon balm leaves to give aroma and to polish, while fresh horsetail was used to bring metal utensils to a brilliant shine.

Today, these herbs can be used to make your own cleaning products.

### Horsetail Metal Cleaner

An all-purpose metal cleaner can be made from the herb Horsetail (*Equisetum arvense*). Horsetail is easily grown in the home garden and can be purchased ready to plant from herb nurseries and some general nurseries.

To make the cleaner you will need:

*250 g fresh horsetail*
*4 cups (1 litre) water*

Steep the herb in cold water overnight, then boil for 15 minutes. Leave to cool, strain and bottle.

Rub metal pieces with a cloth soaked in the solution and leave to dry. Polish with a soft rag.

### General-purpose Cleaner

*10 ml eucalyptus oil*
*3 ml lavender oil*

*20 ml methylated spirits*
*2 cups (500 ml) water*

Dissolve eucalyptus oil and lavender oil in methylated spirits. Add to a pump-spray bottle filled with water and shake well to mix.

Spray on surface and wipe off with a clean, soft cloth.

*See also Bathroom, Bicarbonate of Soda, Dishwashing, Disinfectant, Floors (Cleaning), Furniture Polish, Iron, Kettles, Laminex, Laundry, Marble, Oven, Pastry Boards, Saucepans, Silverware, Soap, Stainless Steel, Stains, Windows.*

## CLOTHES MOTHS

It can be devastating to find out that a favourite jumper or expensive woollen suit has been a banquet for moth larvae. You can use a spray to protect your clothes and other woollen items, or easily obtained camphor balls. However, both these choices are poisonous. They can easily be avoided as there are various natural alternatives which will work just as well.

Herbs have been used for centuries as protection against clothes moths, and among the most successful are lavender, rosemary, southernwood, cotton lavender (santolina), and woodruff. Other herbs that are effective in blends are pieces of elecampane root, orris, roseroot, tansy, thyme and spearmint.

Spices can also be used: cloves, caraway seeds, nutmeg, mace, cinnamon, tonka beans and dried lemon peel. Combined and prepared as a dry potpourri the herbs are added to muslin or coarsely woven cotton or linen bags and placed in drawers and cupboards amongst woollens and other clothes. They can also be slipped into the pockets of suits and jackets or hung on coathangers or wardrobe rails.

Check the scent of your moth bags every 6 months, and if not strong enough mix up a new batch. Use only dried herbs and ingredients.

### Moth Repellent Sachet
You can make a very effective repellent mix by blending together the following herbs and spices:

*25 g tansy*
*25 g rosemary*
*25 g wormwood*
*15 g freshly crushed cloves*
*2 tablespoons orrisroot powder (from chemist)*

Using your hands thoroughly mix all the ingredients in
a large ceramic bowl. Add the mix to a plastic bag, seal it airtight,
and leave to cure in a dry, dark spot for 6 weeks. Wash your
hands thoroughly afterwards before touching food or your face.
Give the mix a good shake every other day.

Place the mixture in small sachets and sew the ends together.

## OTHER CONTROL METHODS

• Seal clothes or blankets in plastic bags and hang them in the sun
for a day. This will kill any moths and their eggs.
• Sprinkle Epsom salts through wardrobes, drawers and linen
cupboards.
• Soak a cloth in turpentine and thoroughly rub all internal wood
surfaces of drawers and wardrobes, including joints and crevices.
• Scatter dried orange peel or lemon peel in drawers and
cupboards as a deterrent.
• Crumble together cinnamon bark pieces, dried wormwood
leaves and the dried leaves of tansy and mint and put into muslin
bags to help keep moths from cupboards and drawers.

*See also Laundry (Moth Repellent Rinse and Fragrant Rinse).*

## COCKROACHES

Most people tend to shudder when they think of cockroaches
scuttling around their kitchen after the lights go out, crawling over
dishes and invading cupboards, drawers and food packages. And
for good reason — cockroaches are disease carriers.

However, these pests can be controlled without resorting to
chemical bombardment:

• Dust a thick layer of diatomaceous earth wherever they are
    suspected of congregating. The microscopic fragments of the
    powder grind away at the carapaces, eventually causing
    death from dehydration.

- Sprinkle boracic acid or eucalyptus oil in cupboards and corners, or dust borax around the refrigerator and stove areas. Pyrethrum powder or oil is also effective.
- Leave bottle caps of 5 per cent borax in sugar wherever they are suspected of gathering.
- Mix together 2 cups (500 g) of cold mashed potato and 1 tablespoon of baking powder and form into balls the size of marbles. Place 2 to 3 balls where cockroaches gather, leaving a few balls around for future generations.

Keep renewing until left untouched. This bait reacts with the insects' body heat and blows them apart.

### COCKROACH TRAP

Provided there is no other easily accessible food around, this trap works very effectively and only requires empty jam jars or the like.

Smear the inside top third of the jar with lard or margarine (this stops them from escaping), add a little cooking oil, just enough to cover the bottom, and then a piece of banana, glob of vegemite, etc.

Locate traps in cupboards, near the refrigerator, by the garbage bin, or wherever else cockroaches may be. In the morning pour boiling water in your traps to kill them.

## COFFEE SUBSTITUTE

*See Dietary Substitutes.*

## COLDS AND 'FLU

### FIGHTING THE COMMON COLD

When winter arrives, many people, despite their best efforts at prevention, suffer the miseries of the common cold. There is nothing worse: it is Nature's way of telling you your body is under too much stress and you need to slow down.

So if your best efforts at prevention do not work, the following advice will help to alleviate the symptoms.

- Drink a cup of hot herb tea every hour or so. Blend equal parts of dried peppermint, elderflower and yarrow and brew in a ceramic pot — 1 teaspoon for each person and one for the pot. Steep for 5 minutes, strain and sip slowly.

Try it as a hot toddy: add lemon juice, honey and a liberal dash of whisky.

• Inhale a herbal steam to relieve nasal congestion and catarrh.

Add 3 drops of peppermint oil, 1 drop of sage oil and 1 drop of thyme oil to a ceramic bowl half filled with boiling water. Hold your face about 30 cm away, and cover your head with a towel large enough to form a tent and not allow vapour to escape. Do not steam for any longer than 10 minutes. Do not use this procedure if you have very fine skin or sensitive skin.

Other head-clearing oils are eucalyptus and tea tree.

• Add a few drops of peppermint oil to a bowl of warm water, as a protection against bacteria, and leave in your bedroom on a table away from the window.

• Ease a sore throat by gargling with Sage Gargle or Rose Petal Throat Soother as required.

## Sage Gargle

*100 g fresh (or 30 g dried) sage leaves*
*2 cups (500 ml) water*
*honey*

Steep the herb in boiling water for 10 minutes, strain, cool and add honey to taste.

## Rose Petal Throat Soother

*1 cup rose petals (fresh or dried)*
*200 g honey*

Put ingredients in a bowl, place in a shallow pan of boiling water and simmer for 10 minutes. Strain and store in a sealed jar.

Either sip a teaspoonful or add to warm water and gargle.

• Ease a cough with Violet Cough Syrup (a good expectorant for children). *See Violets.*
• Go to bed early.
  *See also Throat Lozenge.*

## Herbal Chest Rub

To ease chest congestion, rub the following ointment liberally onto the skin around the upper chest and neck, just prior to going to bed.

½ handful dried horseradish root (or horseradish powder)
200 g Vaseline

Reduce the horseradish root to a powder by rubbing through a fine metal sieve or processing in a blender. (Powdered horseradish is available from most health food stores.) Horseradish can 'burn' sensitive skin, so do a patch test first if you might have this problem.

Put the Vaseline in a small bowl and place it in a pan of boiling water. Stir until melted and then add the horseradish, stirring until well blended. Simmer for 20 minutes, remove from heat and store in a sterilised glass jar.

*See also First Aid, Bath (Therapeutic), Garlic, Headache, Pain, Teas (Herbal).*

**Did you know ...**
that at the first sign of a cold or 'flu, symptoms can be alleviated by adding one drop of eucalyptus or tea tree oil to a glass of warm water and gargling?

## COMPANION PLANTING

Spring is the time for gardens to be planted out for the delicious glut of summer vegetables, a time when all those nasty pests appear to feast on young seedlings.

You can quite easily reach for a chemical spray that's guaranteed to get rid of them, along with everything else that lives in your garden. However, there are much safer alternatives to 'garden genocide'.

Instead of monoculture — planting of a mass of one species together — make mixed plantings for mutual protection. Plant your herbs and vegetables together to repel insect attack and to promote the growth and flavour of your vegetables. You will be working with Nature and not against it, encouraging friendly species of insects and other creatures to live in your garden and feed on those you wish to eradicate.

Tomatoes grow well near asparagus, celery, parsley, basil, carrots and chives. Basil planted between rows will repel white fly, French marigolds growing nearby will keep nematodes at bay, and stinging nettles will protect them from mould. Carefully dig up and transplant one or two amongst your tomato plants.

Melons grow well between rows of sweet corn, as do squash and cucumbers. Sweet corn grown near tomatoes will lure the pest Heliothis from them.

Summer savory planted between rows of beans will inhibit the bean beetle. Onions appreciate summer savory too. Sage protects carrots against carrot fly, as do alternate rows of leeks. Sage will also keep the white butterfly away from cabbages.

All plants growing near thyme are invigorated by it. When thyme is grown near plants of the cabbage family, it will repel cabbage-root fly. Nasturtiums growing amongst vegetables will drive away aphids, keep away cucumber beetles, and when planted near radishes will give them a good hot taste.

Lemon balm attracts bees to the garden and can be used as a border edging in combination with calendulas or French marigolds. Marigolds drive away all manner of pests because of their strong and unpleasant odour. Rue is another herb that insects won't go near and slugs avoid. It makes a useful edging hedge, less than a metre high, and is easily grown from seed. Keep it away from sage and basil, they don't mix.

Working with Nature will reward you with healthier produce.

## COMPOST

Composting is the biological reduction of organic wastes to humus: a rich humus with a slightly sweet, earthy aroma.

A healthy heap needs both water and air to generate the heat required to hasten the breaking-down process. If allowed to dry out the process will slow; likewise, if air cannot circulate, the entire process will take much longer and may even stop.

Effective compost should be built layer upon layer, alternating food wastes with an activator such as animal manure, blood and bone, or liquid seaweed. The nitrogen and protein content of the activator accelerates the breakdown of the organic matter and encourages the bacteria to heat up the heap.

## MAKING YOUR COMPOST HEAP

Clear a patch of ground — remove grass and level if necessary. Compost should always be built on soil and never on concrete.

Scatter a few bricks placed edge down within the cleared area to allow air to circulate into the heap.

Put down your first layer of material — grass clippings, garden wastes, kitchen scraps, and so on in the middle. Next dust over a layer of fowl or cow manure, dolomite or blood and bone to a depth of about 1 cm. Sprinkle with water. Repeat this procedure until your pile is built. After a week, turn the pile over with a fork to speed up decomposition.

A compost pile about one metre in height should be broken down into humus after 2 months in summer, but longer in winter. Add to garden soil in spring and autumn at the rate of 1 kg per square metre, or a 5 cm covering over the garden bed. It can also be used for container plants, raising seedlings and mulching around growing plants.

## UNDERGROUND COMPOSTING

If you don't have a compost bin or heap, simply dig a hole in the garden, fill it with kitchen scraps, sprinkle a cup of dolomite over it, and cover again with soil. After a couple of weeks or so earthworms will have the soil workable, giving you a high-quality humus.

## TIN CANS

You can compost tins after crushing by placing them in a shallow hole, then covering with a 15 to 20 cm layer of dirt. Keep building up alternate layers until approximately 30 to 45 cm above ground level, finishing off with a good thick layer of mulch over the whole of the mound.

After approximately 12 months the tin cans will have completely decomposed, leaving a friable compost.

## COOKING

### BOUQUET GARNI

Crumble some dried bay leaf, dried thyme, dried marjoram and dried parsley and put in the middle of a muslin square. Tie with piece of long string for easy removal at the end of the cooking time.

A useful gift for those who like to cook. Place about 6 sachets in a cellophane square and tie into a bag with a piece of ribbon.

## Peppermint-geranium Jelly Conserve

This is an unusual, yet delicious tasting conserve made from peppermint-scented geranium leaves. You may, of course, use any of the other many types of scented geraniums: spicy, nutmeg, lime, apple, ginger, rose or coconut.

*1 cup (100 g) stalkless peppermint-scented geranium leaves*
*5 cups (1.1 kg) caster sugar*
*juice of 1 lemon*
*4 cups (1 litre) water*
*125 g powdered pectin*
*Crème de Menthe for colouring*

Wash the geranium leaves and steep them in the sugar and lemon juice for 1 hour. Place in a saucepan with the water and bring to boil. Strain, add the pectin (follow instructions on packet), and boil again, stirring for about 1 minute. Add the Crème de Menthe and pour into clean glass jars, placing a small geranium leaf in each one. Seal the lids.

It will keep in the refrigerator for several weeks. If you want to keep it longer than this, process with a bottling outfit, such as Fowlers Vacola.

*See also Dietary Substitutes, Yeast.*

# VACUUM FLASK COOKING

Winter meals, such as rice, vegetables stews and oats, can be effectively cooked in a wide-mouthed vacuum flask — a great energy saver.

It will keep food hot for hours and save hot water. It can be used to soak dried grains, vegetables and legumes, and can be used to cook in by simply adding hot water.

## RICE AND VEGETABLE STEW

Add diced vegetables, rice, lentils and stock to a saucepan. Bring to the boil, allow to boil for about 2 minutes, and then pour into your vacuum flask. Cap and leave for 3 to 4 hours to cook.

## WINTER BREAKFAST

Put 1 cup (155 g) of wheat or oats in a flask, add 4 cups (1 litre) of boiling water about 12 hours before the time you want breakfast. Strain off in the morning and serve with honey, sultanas, raisins and diced seasonal fruit.

Soak raisins and sultanas overnight, and add soaking water to the breakfast if you wish.

## COOLING

### MAKING THE MOST OF DECIDUOUS PLANTS

Plants can be used to form living blinds for your windows that will give the inside of your house a cool, greenish, broken light.

Deciduous vines, such as grapes, are useful if grown on the western side (eastern side in northern hemisphere) of the house on a high, free-standing pergola above window height. Grape vines will also provide a valuable mulch in the form of leaves in autumn.

North-facing (south-facing in the northern hemisphere) windows can be shaded by a 'window pergola', which is no more than an extended window box with a lattice or individual lengths of wire running from it to the top of the window frame. Crops like climbing beans will provide shade, plus the additional benefit of a vegetable. Leave the window box free for a splash of colour from winter flowers.

Cool evening breezes can be deflected into the house in summer, to give relief in hot humid conditions, by a high continuous, free-standing trellis. Again grow grapes or any of the other rambling vine or cane fruits: passionfruit, loganberry, youngberry and boysenberry.

The best distribution of cross ventilation is achieved by allowing the breeze in through a smaller, low-level opening, and letting it out through a larger opening on the downwind side.

### LAWNS AND HEDGES

The lawn has a lot going for it as a climate modifier. Combined with other greenery around your house it has a definite cooling effect. And if you shudder at the thought of spending all that time sweating in the heat to keep the lawn in trim, replace it with a thyme lawn (drought hardy), Dichonrad, or lawn chamomile in cooler areas.

Hedges can be planted to eliminate road glare and paths can be replaced by paving stones with ground cover plants — thyme, chamomile, pennyroyal — growing between them. As the plants spread, the glare of the stone is reduced and eventually eliminated. Try different varieties of thyme — caraway, woolly and Shakespearean — combined with chamomile for a variety of colour, and wormwood or yew for a tall hedge.

## REDUCING INTERNAL HEAT GAIN

No matter how effectively your home is insulated against external heat gain, heat generated by people, lights and appliances can still contribute to uncomfortable internal living temperatures. Instead of using a high energy-consuming air conditioner to maintain comfortable living conditions, modify your household habits:

• Try to prepare meals that use minimum stove cooking time, or require no cooking at all.
• Avoid using the oven — if baking, do this in the cool of the evening when breezes can blow away heat, or in the early morning before the heat of the day starts.
• Consider using a microwave oven if you don't already have one. They not only save on energy, but do not contribute significantly to internal heat gain.
• On hot days keep windows and external doors closed, lower external blinds or awnings, and draw internal blinds or curtains. Close internal doors which lead to areas likely to be influenced by outside conditions. Instead of using an air conditioner in hot weather, open the windows and let the natural breeze cool you.
• If possible locate refrigerators and freezers in a garage, laundry or on a verandah.

Simple solar modifications will allow them to stay in the kitchen: install a screened, closeable vent in the floor behind the appliance and a vent in the ceiling above it, connected to a length of copper or stainless steel flue pipe. The flue should extend about a metre above the roof where it exits, and be fitted with a screened, weatherproof cap.

The hot air from the appliance is exhausted up the flue by convection, and cooler air to replace it is drawn from under the house. During the heat of the day the flue will heat up and functions as a small heat pump, making the system even more effective.

## NATURAL WATER-COOLED AIR CONDITIONING

This is, without doubt, one of the easiest methods of cooling, relying on evaporation for instant water-cooled air conditioning.

Large pots of water (covered with insect wire to prevent mosquitoes breeding) placed below windows where the draft will flow over them will provide instant, water-cooled air conditioning.

Or select a few medium to large round goldfish bowls, add a layer of dirt, root in some water plants, fill with water, and place them below windows where a breeze will blow across the top of them.

Fish ponds underneath pergolas and in a line close to access doors will have the same effect.

All three ideas work on the same principle as energy-hungry air conditioners, but they are simple and energy efficient.

## COPPER STAINS

Mix 1 tablespoon of salt with 1 cup (250 ml) of white vinegar. Dip half a lemon in this solution and rub vigorously on the stain or tarnish.

The entire copper surface can be brought to a brilliant shine in this way.

## COUGHS

*See First Aid, Throat Lozenge, Violets.*

## CRADLE CAP

*See First Aid.*

## CREAM

*Did you know ...*

that cream makes an excellent skin cleanser? Smooth well into your skin, leave for a few minutes, rinse with tepid water and then with cold water. Pat your face dry with a soft towel.

If your skin tends to be oily, add a few drops of lemon juice to the cream.

## CREAM SUBSTITUTES

*See Dietary Substitutes.*

## CROP ROTATION

*See Garden.*

## CURTAINS

### Stain Removal Solution

Stains on curtains can be spot-cleaned with following solution:

*4 tablespoons dried soapwort*
*distilled water, sufficient*

Put soapwort in an enamel or stainless steel pan and add enough water to cover. Boil for 10 minutes, remove from heat and allow to steep until cold. Strain through fine muslin and store in a tightly sealed bottle.

This solution will keep up to 7 days if kept in the refrigerator. To extend its keeping qualities, add 2 teaspoons of methylated spirits to every 2 cups (500 ml), or part thereof, of the solution.

### Dust and Odours

Soak curtains in vinegar, then wash.

## CUTS AND ABRASIONS

*See Antiseptic, First Aid, Pets (Cuts and Abrasions).*

## DANDELION (*TARAXALUM OFFICINALE*)

This common wild herb, which can be found throughout most of the temperate world, is a virtual storehouse of vitamins, minerals, enzymes, proteins and other valuable elements, making it a wholesome plant food.

Taken regularly as a tea it adds a healthy bloom to the complexion and acts as a general tonic to the body systems. The root can be dried, roasted and ground, and makes an excellent caffeine-free substitute for coffee.

### Dandelion Coffee Substitute

Gather roots in autumn, wash and dry them, and cut into rings about 2 cm thick. Dry in the sun on drying trays (muslin stretched tight over a timber frame will suffice). Do not leave them out overnight where they will attract moisture. Once completely dry roast the pieces in a hot oven (200°C) for 20 minutes. Reduce to granules in a coffee bean grinder or blender, and store in an airtight jar. Use in the same way as instant coffee.

## DANDRUFF

*See Hair Care.*

## DEODORANT

An effective deodorant can be made by steeping herbs in cider vinegar. It will have both a subdued perfume and antiseptic properties, and will keep you feeling fresh and odour-free.

Herbs suitable for making deodorant vinegars are: lavender, sage, lovage, eau-de-cologne mint, spearmint, scented geranium leaves, rosemary, thyme, marjoram and honeysuckle.

### Herbal Deodorant

*9 tablespoons fresh herb (or mixture) of your choice*
*cider vinegar*

Put the herbs in a large, wide-mouthed glass jar. Gently warm sufficient cider vinegar to cover the herbs, pour into jar, seal tightly, and leave where it will receive plenty of hot sun for 2 weeks. Shake the contents every day. Strain the vinegar and store in a tightly capped bottle for future use.

If the scent is not strong enough, repeat the process, using the same vinegar, with a fresh batch of herbs.

To make your liquid deodorant dilute 1 teaspoon of herb vinegar with 2 tablespoons of distilled water. Store in an airtight glass bottle.

After washing and drying under arms, dab on the deodorant and allow to dry.

This type of deodorant will last indefinitely and does not need to be stored in the refrigerator.

## DIARRHOEA

*See First Aid.*

## DIETARY SUBSTITUTES

A change in our daily diet for health reasons does not have to be devastating. Try some of these substitutes which are healthy and natural.

### COFFEE SUBSTITUTE

You can purchase dandelion coffee substitute from your local health food store. Alternatively, you can make your own from ground dandelion roots. *See Dandelion.*

### DAIRY SUBSTITUTES
**Dairy-free Butter**
Use the following herbal spread:

*dried herbs of your choice or garlic*
*4 tablespoons food yeast*
*1 teaspoon powdered kelp*
*olive oil*

Mince the garlic and reduce chosen dried herbs to a powder by rubbing through a fine metal sieve.

Mix all ingredients together, using sufficient olive oil to form a butter-like consistency, and process in a blender. Store in a suitable airtight container in the refrigerator.

## Dairy-free Cheese
This makes a soft cottage-cheese-like cheese substitute.

*1 cup (125 g) unsalted cashew nuts*
*⅔ cup (120 g) sunflower seeds*
*1 cup (250 ml) water*
*dried seasoning herbs, to taste*

Process nuts and seeds in a blender until fine, doing small amounts at a time. Fold water in slowly to make a smooth, thick batter.

Ferment by allowing the mixture to stand for 12 to 24 hours at 20 to 25°C until of a fluffy consistency. Add seasoning herbs of your choice and refrigerate for several hours before using.

## Dairy-free Cream

*½ cup (90 g) almonds*
*1 cup (250 ml) water*
*1 tablespoon honey*
*¼ cup (60 ml) cold pressed corn oil*

Chop the almonds into small pieces and process with water and honey in a blender, then add oil in a thin stream.

## Milk Substitutes
Soya milk, either fresh or powdered, is a healthy substitute for dairy milk. Fruit juices are delicious on breakfast cereals and muesli and can be used in baking in place of milk.

You can make your own seed/nut milk from sunflower or sesame seeds or almond and cashew nuts.

*½ cup (90 g) selected seeds*
*1 to 2 cups (250 to 500 ml) water*

Place seeds in a blender, grind, then add water and process at high speed till smooth and creamy.

Use as is to pour over cereals or smoothies (blend with fruit and/or fruit juice), or strain to make a thinner milk for use in beverages, such as coffee substitutes.

## Sunflower Milk Smoothie

*4 cups (800 g) sunflower seeds*
*3 to 4 bananas, peeled and sliced*
*a few slices fresh papaya*
*flesh of 1 to 2 passionfruit*

Combine all the ingredients in a blender and process them until they are smooth.

## Salt Substitute

Salt is an inorganic substance that is not a food, and is not utilised by the body. It will cause stiffening of the joints, arthritis, hardening of the arteries and kidney disease.

Salt was one of the ingredients used by the ancient Egyptians to embalm their dead. If it is taken in high enough concentrations it will inhibit cell metabolism, and can eventually cause the death of the cells.

You can replace salt as a condiment with a herbal substitute, and including kelp in this substitute will still give you the salty taste that is so popular.

The following herb seasoning is easy to make, but like all condiments, it should be used with discrimination so as to not overpower the natural flavour of the food. All ingredients are available from your local health food store.

*1 tablespoon dried celery seeds*
*1 tablespoon dried thyme*
*1 tablespoon dried oregano*
*2 tablespoons dried kelp*
*1 tablespoon dried toasted sesame seeds*

Combine all ingredients, mixing well, and reduce to a powder in a blender or by rubbing through a fine wire sieve.

When mixed, store in an airtight jar. Label and date the jar and use the seasoning within 12 months.

## SUGAR SUBSTITUTES

Ideal replacements for sugar are:

• Molasses — contains more minerals per same quantity of honey
• Honey
• Treacle — a more refined form of molasses
• Dates — very sweet and can be used in breakfast foods, such as porridge
• Dried fruits such as apricots and sultanas may be added to either raw or cooked food.

## FABULOUS FRUIT

There are no shortcuts to eating well. Popping vitamin pills is no real help if your diet is poor.

The way we eat largely determines our energy levels through the day.

To feel great and to look good, the key is to eat for energy. Include lots of raw fruits and vegetables in your daily diet for maximum vitality.

Eat less highly processed, ready-in-a-minute foods loaded with chemical additives and more natural foods. Do this, and your energy levels will begin to soar.

### Fruit Salad

Use the following fresh fruits when they are in season:

*1 small pineapple, diced*
*2 peaches, sliced*
*2 medium mangoes, sliced (when in season)*
*2 pears, diced*
*2 oranges, diced*
*1 apple, diced*
*375 g ricotta cheese, crumbled*

Place the prepared fruit in a bowl, then add the cheese and stir slightly until the fruit is evenly distributed, then chill and serve.

As a luncheon meal this is complete in itself, supplying abundant protein, vitamins and minerals.

## Soya/Fruit Ice Cream

Another way we can enjoy the succulent sweetness of fresh fruits is a fruit salad topped with ice cream. However, commercially produced ice-creams are in many cases are loaded with chemicals.

Why not make your own? The following recipe is quick and simple to make, and is healthy and delicious.

*6 large, very ripe bananas, peeled and chopped*
*1 cup (250 ml) cold pressed vegetable oil*
*6 tablespoons soya milk powder*
*2 tablespoons honey*
*1 cup (250 ml) water*
*2 tablespoons fine carob powder*

Place bananas, oil, honey, soya milk powder, water and carob powder in a food processor or blender and process until smooth. Pour into a freezerproof container, cover and freeze until firm.

This ice-cream does not require beating during freezing and will keep indefinitely. If it does thaw, it can be refrozen once without any loss of flavour or quality.

## DISHWASHING

### Dishwashing Gel

This biodegradable gel will remove grease and grime and still be gentle on your hands.

*4 tablespoons dried soapwort*
*4 tablespoons dried lemon verbena*
*9 litres water*
*½ cake pure soap, grated*
*½ cup (120 g) washing soda*

Place the herbs in a large bucket and add 8 litres of boiling water. Cover, steep overnight, then strain through muslin.

Add grated soap and a little of the reserved water to a pan, bring to the boil, reduce heat and stir constantly until soap has dissolved. Boil remaining water and add this, plus the washing soda, to another bucket, stirring until all the soda has dissolved. Add soap mixture and herbal infusion, mixing thoroughly.

The mixture will set into a soft gel and can be stored for future use. Use ¼ to ½ cup (125 to 250 ml) of the gel for washing dishes.

2 tablespoons of pure soap flakes dissolved in hot water is also adequate for most smaller dishwashing jobs.

## USEFUL TIPS

• Don't throw away the mesh bags when you buy oranges. Insert a piece of foam, tie the ends of the bag into a knot, and use as a scourer.
• A few drops of lemon juice added to the water will make glass shine and remove stains from porcelain.
• To remove tough grease, add a dash of vinegar to the soapy water or wash dishes with bicarbonate of soda.
• For dirty saucepans and tannin stains in cups and teapots, see Bicarbonate of Soda.

*See also Lemon, Loofah, Saucepans.*

## DISINFECTANT

Any of the herbs in the following list can be used. They are listed in descending order of their antiseptic power: lemon, tea tree, thyme, orange, bergamot, juniper, clove, lavender, peppermint, rosemary, sandalwood and eucalyptus.

Use the following disinfectant to wipe over sinks, toilet bowls, baths and kitchen benchtops.

### Herbal Disinfectant

*6 drops lemon oil*
*6 drops eucalyptus oil*
*1 teaspoon methylated spirits*
*8 cups (2 litres) tepid water*

Dissolve the essential oils in the alcohol and add to tepid water (hot water will make the oils evaporate too quickly).

*See also Antiseptic, Oven (Disinfectant Cleaning Liquid).*

**Did you know ...**
that an effective natural disinfectant can be made from onions and cider vinegar?

To a large container add the juice of several onions (which have been salted and left overnight), 1 cup (250 ml) of cider vinegar, 4 drops each of rosemary oil and lavender oil, and 8 cups (2 litres) of water. Shake well to mix and store for future use.

## DOG WASHING SOAP

A good soap for washing the family dog that will help to control fleas.

*100 g Vaseline*
*fresh pennyroyal*
*80 g beeswax*
*300 g soap flakes*
*100 g methylated spirits*

Infuse half a handful of pennyroyal to every 100 grams of Vaseline. Finely chop the herb; put the Vaseline into a double pan and melt the Vaseline over a medium heat. Add the herb and simmer for twenty minutes.

Stir in the wax and when melted add the soap flakes, stirring until completely dissolved. Remove from heat and immediately stir in the alcohol. Pour into moulds to harden and cut into bars.

This soap can be used immediately.

*See also Fleas.*

## DRAINS

To clear sluggish drains pour in ½ cup (140 g) of baking soda followed by ½ cup (125 ml) of vinegar, then plug the drain and let the two substances react with each other. Unplug the drain and run the hot water tap for 3 minutes.

*See also Bicarbonate of Soda.*

## EARACHE

*See First Aid.*

## EARTHWORMS

Garden soil that is alive with earthworms is rich and productive. Soil depleted by overuse, excessive chemical abuse, or lacking in organic material will contain very few, if any, earthworms.

Their addition to the soil will not instantly give you a rich, friable humus, but they will certainly assist in restoring a balance. And combined with added compost, manure and organic fertiliser the earthworms will rapidly multiply, gradually improving your soil.

## ELDER TREE (*SAMBUCUS NIGRA*)

To most country folk the elder tree is known as the 'medicine chest', since all parts of the tree can be utilised and are rich in vitamins. It is an evergreen tree growing from 3 to 10 metres in height with rough, cork-like bark. The foliage consists of delicate, dark green leaves with finely jagged edges and flat clusters of sweet-smelling, yellowish-cream flowers that develop the dark red berries.

A tea of fresh or dried flowers is an ideal spring tonic for purifying the blood, and when the roots are used the tea imparts a gentle laxative effect and is excellent for constipation. Equal parts of the dried flowers, peppermint and yarrow is a traditional tea for treating the miseries of colds and 'flu.

Elder water makes an excellent face lotion that is mildly astringent and is particularly good to use after a cleanser. Made into a soothing ointment it will relieve facial soreness due to exposure to sea air, and can be used for chapped hands and insect bites.

Included in the bath it is both healing and stimulating, in hand creams it will help to repair damaged skin and keep it supple, and when used as a facial steam will tighten pores.

## Elderflower Soothing Lotion

Use for facial soreness due to exposure to sea air.

*1 teaspoon dried elderflowers*
*1 cup (250 ml) boiling water*
*2 tablespoons glycerine*
*¼ teaspoon triethanalomine (from chemist)*

Put the dried elderflowers in a ceramic bowl and add boiling water. Steep until cool, strain through fine muslin, gently warm and blend ⅔ cup (150 ml) of the solution with the glycerine and triethanalomine, stirring until they are well mixed. Store the lotion in a tightly sealed jar.

Apply to face whenever required.

## Elderflower Ointment

Apply to chapped hands and insect bites.

*1 tablespoon dried elderflowers*
*100 g jar Vaseline*

Melt the Vaseline in a small bowl standing in a pan of boiling water. Add the elderflowers, simmer for 30 minutes, and then strain through muslin. Store in a sterilised glass jar with a tight fitting lid.

## ELDERFLOWER LOTION

This toning lotion is suitable for all skin types and is both healing and soothing to the skin.

*3 tablespoons dried elderflowers*
*1¼ cups (300 ml) cider vinegar*
*1¼ cups (300 ml) distilled water*

Put the herbs in a wide-mouthed glass jar. Mix together the cider vinegar and distilled water and heat to just below boiling point. Pour the liquid over the herbs, cover tightly with plastic wrap and leave to steep for 12 hours. Strain and dilute with a further ⅔ cup (150 ml) of distilled water and bottle for future use.

To use the toning lotion, pour a small amount onto slightly damp cottonwool, and gently apply to face and neck using an outward and upward movement.

## Elderflower 'Champagne'

Although this delightful, fizzy summer drink is called champagne, it is non-alcoholic and can be enjoyed by all the family.

*3 sprays elderflowers*
*1 lemon*
*3 cups (600 g) sugar*
*2 tablespoons white wine vinegar*
*18 cups (4½ litres) water*

Carefully remove the flowers from the stems with scissors and place them in a large ceramic crock or enamel pan. Add the juice and thinly peeled rind of the lemon, sugar, wine vinegar and water and leave for 48 hours. Strain through clean muslin into a tightly-sealed glass bottle. Allow to stand for 2 weeks before drinking.

## ELECTRIC JUGS AND KETTLES

*See Kettles.*

## ENGINE OIL

*See Oil.*

## ESSENTIAL OILS

Whether you inhale them, add them to your bath, dab them on the skin, or include them in a massage oil, pure essential aromatic oils are extremely beneficial. Their rich, fragrant perfumes calm, soothe, heal, fight infection, revitalise, relax and stimulate the body.

The oils are very concentrated and so only a small amount, a few drops, is necessary. Try the following tips:

### INDIGESTION AND NAUSEA

Add 1 drop of peppermint oil to a glass of warm water with a little honey and sip. It acts extremely quickly. This also works well to counteract nausea during pregnancy.

### DIFFICULT BREATHING

A few drops of eucalyptus or peppermint oil on your handkerchief will ease difficult breathing when inhaled.

## MUSCULAR PAIN

Massage 6 drops of eucalyptus oil and 6 drops of lavender oil, mixed together, into the painful area.

## REVITALISATION

Revitalise yourself after an extra busy day by adding a few drops of ylang ylang oil and bergamot to a warmish bath and soaking it for ten minutes. Unwind with a mixture of lavender and rosewood oils in your evening bath.

Help to revitalise your body and restore health after illness by adding tangerine oil to your bath or take it as an inhalation. It's also good for a soothing back massage for anxiety or for expectant mothers, and helps to improve energy levels.

*For blemished skin and face cleanser, see Lavender.*

*See also Air Fresheners, Bath, Car Freshener, Feet, Headache, Insect Repellents, Lice, Stress, Xmas.*

*Did you know ...*

that eucalyptus oil is a powerful antiseptic, and also generates ozone when exposed to the air?

To disinfect and freshen a sick room, place a cotton ball dipped in eucalyptus oil on a small dish away from drafts or an open window.

## FACE

*See Kaolin, Skin Care.*

## FEET

### COLD FEET

Put on a hat to warm your feet.

A woollen cap or a beanie is a must when out-of-doors in cold weather. If your head is cold, your feet, hands and the rest of your body will also be cold.

Blood is pumped up to warm the head at the expense of reduced flow — and reduced warmth — to other parts of the body.

### ESSENTIAL OILS FOR FEET

**Persistent soreness**

You can relieve persistent soreness by massaging the following oil generously into feet after soaking them, or after your bath.

Blend 10 drops each of calendula, oregano and lime oils with 2 tablespoons almond oil, 1 teaspoon wheatgerm oil and 1 teaspoon avocado oil. Store in an amber-coloured, airtight glass bottle until needed. Use within 3 months.

### SWEATY FEET

Bathe them in a bowl of hot water containing a few drops of lemongrass oil. Pat dry, then rub in a mixture of 3 drops lemongrass oil to 1 teaspoon soya oil.

Also good for tinea (Athlete's foot).

### TINEA (ATHLETE'S FOOT)

Soak feet in warm water to which has been added 6 to 10 drops of tea tree oil or lavender oil. For persistent cases, paint with neat oil and place a cottonwool ball, moistened with several drops of oil, in your shoes at night.

# FENNEL

## WRINKLE MASK

*1 teaspoon fennel seeds*
*1 cup (250 ml) boiling water*
*1 tablespoon unprocessed honey*
*3 tablespoons plain yoghurt*

Put the fennel seeds in a ceramic bowl, add the boiling water and infuse until cold. Strain and mix with the other ingredients.

Apply to the face, avoiding the eyes, and leave on for 15 minutes. Lie down while the face pack is on. Wash off with warm water, then splash face with cold water and pat dry with a soft towel.

# FERTILISER

Fresh or dried poultry manure can make a rich liquid garden fertiliser with a high nitrogen content.

Quarter fill a large plastic garbage bin, or a clean 200 litre drum that has had one end removed, with manure and water. Cover with a lid to keep the smell and flies away. After 2 weeks the liquid will be ready for use. Dilute with 3 parts fresh water and pour around plants once every 2 weeks. Leftover sludge can be added to your compost heap or used as a mulch.

With seaweed, you can also prepare a spray that will fertilise your plants and help control fungus.

Rinse away all traces of salt first. Use the same quantity as you did manure, steep for 3 weeks and dilute with 2 parts of fresh water.

## URINE FERTILISER

If it doesn't worry you to collect, human urine is a good source of nitrogen, provided that it has been diluted first. It is essential that no-one in the family is suffering from any major medical problem.

Dilute 1 part urine with 5 parts water and apply to soil around plants once or twice a year using a watering can, or add to the compost as an activator.

### Biodynamic Fertiliser

Spray this solution onto soil every 2 weeks during autumn to ensure healthy crops.

*1 teaspoon dried cow manure*
*27 litres rain water*
*1 cup (25 g) dried Fat Hen leaves*
*1 cup (25 g) dried dandelion leaves*
*1 cup (25 g) dried stinging nettles*
*1 cup (25 g) dried purslane leaves*
*1 cup (30 g) dried chamomile*
*1 cup (30 g) dried sage leaves*

Add 4½ litres of rain water to a plastic bucket, stir in the cow manure, cover with clear plastic and allow to stand for 21 days. Strain and then add 1 cup (250 ml) of the concentrate to a container holding the remaining rain water.

Reduce the dried herbs to a powder by rubbing through a fine wire sieve and then add them to the solution. Cover and leave in the sun for 2 days before using.

## FEVERFEW (*TANACETUM PARTHENIUM*)

This small, self-seeding, rather fragrant member of the daisy family is a very old medicinal cottage garden herb. Feverfew makes a very good border plant and it can also be used as an environmentally safe garden insecticide, with an effect similar to that of pyrethrum.

Apart from its general tonic abilities, feverfew is an extremely good preventive for migraine headaches. Eat 3 leaves every day in a sandwich or take as a tea.

Take half a cup of tea every hour at the first sign of migraine attack or tension, or 1 cup every morning as a preventive.

Feverfew can cause mouth dryness, and mouth ulcers, irritation and pain in highly-sensitive individuals.

### Feverfew Tea
Infuse the herb in the following proportions

*1 tablespoon fresh herb or 1 level teaspoon dried herb*
*to 1¼ cups (300 ml) of boiling water*

For individual cups, pour in the hot water, cover, infuse for 3 minutes, and strain into another cup.

If brewing in a teapot allow one serve per individual and one for the pot. Infuse for 5 minutes in boiling water, then strain into individual cups.

Use only a ceramic or glass teapot when you are making herbal tea. Aluminium, or other metals, can quite easily mar the brew.

*See Flea (Flea Spray), Insecticides.*

# FINGERNAILS

Many men and women suffer from brittle fingernails. Usually this type of problem indicates a dietary deficiency.

It is commonly known that calcium is necessary for strong nails, but the mineral silica is equally important. Helpful foods that contain this mineral include barley, kelp, garlic, onions, parsley, rice, chives, celery, lettuce and sunflower seeds.

Dill, horsetail, borage flowers and chives are herbs traditionally used to improve fingernails. They may be taken internally as a tea and used externally as a fingerbath.

## TEA

To make a tea, infuse 6 tablespoons of fresh herb (or 2 teaspoons of dried herb) in a ceramic teapot in 2 cups (500 ml) of boiling water for 7 minutes, then strain into individual cups. Drink 1 cup morning and night. Any excess tea made in the morning can be refrigerated for use later in the day. To speed up the beneficial effect and power of the tea, add a pinch of cayenne.

When using the herb horsetail, you will need to bring it to the boil in an enamel or stainless steel pan and simmer for 30 minutes.

## NAIL BATH

Make a strong infusion of one of the 'fingernail herbs' in a ceramic bowl, steep overnight, strain and store in the refrigerator for up to 5 days.

A suggested strength would be 9 tablespoons of fresh herb or 3 teaspoons of dried herb in 1¼ cups (300 ml) of boiling water.

Soak fingertips in the solution for 15 minutes morning and night.

To keep fingernails supple, massage a little olive oil into them each night after using the herbal nail bath.

*See also Aloe Vera.*

# FIRST AID

How many times has a member of the family cut themselves, been stung by an insect or had an earache and there is no first aid kit handy? Herbs and other simple kitchen remedies can be used successfully as a first aid measure to treat minor complaints and most first aid situations around the home.

## ANTISEPTIC
*See Antiseptic.*

## BEE STINGS
Apply ice directly onto the affected area until both pain and swelling are gone. A honey compress will neutralise the poison and helps pull out the stinger.

## BURNS
Apply iced water, keeping the cloth wet and cold until pain leaves. As an emergency dressing apply the inside of a banana skin, holding in place with a loosely bound bandage.

For simple household burns caused by touching a hot iron or grasping an overheated saucepan handle, gently pat lavender oil onto the affected area.

## COUGH
Mix the juice from ½ lemon with 2 tablespoons of honey and take every 15 minutes.
*See also Colds and Flu.*

## CRADLE CAP
To treat cradle cap in babies, bring ⅓ cup (10 g) of dried chamomile flowers almost to the boil in ⅔ cup (150 ml) of olive oil. Remove from heat, cool and strain into a clean glass bottle.

Rub the oil gently into the scalp, then wash off with warm soapy water.

## CUTS AND ABRASIONS
Apply the inside of a banana skin as directed for burns, or cover with calendula ointment.

## DIARRHOEA

Take ½ teaspoon of nutmeg several times during the day.

After diarrhoea has ceased, eat some grated raw apple or some banana to restore the bowel function to normal.

## EARACHE

Wrap a small onion in foil and grill until soft. Pierce the foil and squeeze out some onion juice. With a dropper, insert 4 to 5 drops of lukewarm juice in the offending ear. Plug with cottonwool and repeat as necessary.

Alternatively, heat two cloves of chopped garlic in 2 teaspoons of olive oil. Strain and then insert a few warm drops in the offending ear. Plug outer ear with cottonwool.

If pain persists, consult your doctor.

## FUNGAL INFECTIONS

Apply a castor oil poultice. Warm about 2 tablespoons of oil to 'blood heat' (body temperature) and smear over the affected area. Cover with a bandage and repeat in a couple of hours if necessary.

A strong and powerful fungicide can be made by blending one part tea tree oil to ten parts water. Use it to treat insect bites and fungal problems such as tinea.

*See (Feet) Tinea.*

## FOREIGN BODIES

For splinters, slivers of glass, bee stings and other foreign bodies, (not in the eye) apply a castor oil poultice as directed for fungal infections.

For foreign bodies in the eye, smear castor oil liberally under the eyelids. Make sure your hands are very clean when you do this. The castor oil will gently form a film and draw and soothe. Offending bodies will be removed along natural channels.

## INSECT BITES

*See Insect Bites and Stings, Mites.*

## Calendula Ointment

A pot of calendula ointment in the first aid cabinet can be used to treat burns, cracked lips, weeping sores, wounds, cuts, abrasions, scratches, grazes and sore nipples, as well as all general skin irritations, including itching, mosquito bite itch and insect bites, and to ease sprains, strains, wrenched ankles and painfulswellings.

*4 tablespoons dried calendula petals*
*distilled water*
*15 g beeswax*
*2 teaspoons aloe vera juice*
*3 tablespoons almond oil*
*2 teaspoons wheatgerm oil*
*6 drops friar's balsam*

Put the calendula petals in a ceramic bowl and cover with 1¼ cups (300 ml) of boiling distilled water. (Bring the distilled water to the boil using an enamel or stainless steel pan.) Cover, steep overnight, strain through muslin.

Melt the beeswax in a double pan over a medium heat until completely liquid. Mix 2 tablespoons of the infusion with the oils and aloe vera juice, gently warm and add to the melted wax, stirring until well blended. Remove from heat, pour into a ceramic mixing bowl, add friar's balsam and beat until cool and creamy. Store in a sterilised glass jar.

## SEDATIVE

Chamomile can be used as a mild sedative to help an active brain go to sleep, to ease menstrual cramps, or to help teething children. Make a tea by pouring 5 tablespoons of boiling water onto 10 g dried chamomile flowers, infuse for an hour and strain.

It can be gently heated to drink hot, and sweetened with honey.
*See also Teas (Herbal).*

## TOOTHACHE

For temporary relief, apply a crushed clove or oil of cloves to the painful tooth, or plug the cavity with cottonwool soaked in the oil.

## TRAVEL SICKNESS

To help ease travel or motion sickness, chop up ½ teaspoon of fresh ginger, dust with powdered cinnamon and bind together with honey. Take before a journey and when symptoms occur.

## WOUNDS

Apply the inside of a banana skin as directed for burns, or use calendula ointment as needed.

*See also Aloe Vera, Colds and 'Flu, Essential Oils, Feet, Headache, Insomnia, Itching, Kitchen Cures, Morning Sickness, Pain, Pets, Sinusitis, Stress, Teas (Herbal).*

## FLEAS

The cause of fleas is most commonly the family pet, and if we keep pets we must be prepared to accept the inevitability of the pests that they carry. It is quite usual for fleas to jump straight from dog or cat to human, making life miserable for the whole household.

Pets leave a lot of detritus — hair, flakes of skin, etc — around for pests to breed in. This will mean more vacuuming, and more airing of rugs to prevent outbreaks.

Weekly hard vacuuming is a must. Do the whole house in 1 day and vacuum lounges, cushions, carpets, mats, up and down curtains, along crevices, and beds and their coverings. Take animal bedding, cushions and mats outside and air them in the sun for a day, then vacuum before bringing them back inside.

Treat carpets, mats and pet bedding with a flea repellent:

• Spray regularly with Cajeput oil solution:
1 teaspoon of oil to every 5 tablespoons of warm water.
• Scatter some dried pennyroyal, cedarwood shavings or pine needles on and under your pet's bedding. Or stuff the bedding material into a large cushion with some dried insect-repelling herbs including pennyroyal, stinking roger, wormwood, tansy or native peppermint.
• Once a week dust with the following Flea Repellent Powder or spray pet's bedding and mats with Flea Spray.

### Flea Repellent Powder

*3 drops pennyroyal oil*
*3 drops eucalyptus oil*
*3 drops cedarwood oil*
*9 drops citronella oil*
*500 g bicarbonate of soda*

Combine the oils and mix them with the bicarbonate of soda. Sprinkle this over carpets, etc., wait 1 hour and then vacuum up.

## Flea Spray

*5 tablespoons feverfew flowers*
*1 tablespoon methylated spirits*
*4 cups (1 litre) boiling water*

Place the flowers in a ceramic bowl, add the boiling water, cover, steep overnight, then strain through muslin, squeezing all liquid from the herbs. Pour into a pump-spray bottle, add the methylated spirits and shake vigorously so that it is well blended.

## Quassia Wash

*30 g quassia chips*
*4 cups (1 litre) water*
*1 teaspoon pennyroyal oil*
*soft soap (from the chemist)*

Boil quassia chips in water for 15 minutes, remove from heat and steep overnight. Strain and add sufficient water to make 8 litres. Make sure you store quassia away from the reach of children, and do not breathe in the fumes when the mixture is boiling.

Mix in pennyroyal oil and just enough soft soap to make a gentle foam. Wash floors with this every two days for a week to kill fleas.

*See also Insect Repellent.*

### GROOMING

Wash animals thoroughly at least once a week, paying particular attention to the areas around the ears, neck, tail, backbone and under the legs. Then comb through a solution of equal parts pennyroyal oil and eucalyptus oil.

Derris also makes an effective, natural flea killer with little residual action, and is ideal for bad infestations.

## After-wash Lotion

*500 g powdered derris*
*½ cup (125 ml) eucalyptus oil*
*methylated spirits*

Combine the powdered derris, eucalyptus oil and enough methylated spirits to make the mixture just liquid. Steep for 3 to 4 days, shaking twice a day, then dilute 1 part lotion to 4 parts water.

Apply a sponge dipped in equal parts of methylated spirits and water to the worst affected areas before applying the derris lotion.

## Flea Powder

In between washes, dust your pet's hair with a herbal flea powder. Derris can be used as a convenient substitute or you can make up the following powder:

*100 g fennel seeds*
*100 g dried pennyroyal*
*100 g dried pyrethrum flowers*

Reduce the fennel seeds to a fine powder using a pestle and mortar, then powder the remaining ingredients by rubbing them through a fine wire sieve. Thoroughly mix all ingredients and store in a suitable container with holes pierced in its lid.

Dust through animal's fur, leave for 30 minutes, then brush or comb it out with a fine-toothed comb. Sweep up dead or stupefied fleas and burn them.

## Derris Wash

Derris powder can also be used as a flea control wash. Just add 30g of powder to every 20 cups (5 litres) of warm soapy water.

Wash the animal thoroughly then rinse with clean water. Apply an after-wash repellent lotion.

*See also Dog Washing Soap.*

## OTHER PREVENTIVE MEASURES

• Include fresh garlic in your pet's daily meal, or simply pop a piece of it down its throat. This will help to build up a natural resistance to fleas.

• 1 teaspoon of powdered sulphur in their food once a week is also reputed to work. This dose is based on an adult cat, which usually weighs around 6 kg, and should be increased or decreased according to weight.

• 6 to 8 drops of pennyroyal oil on your pet's leather collar will help to control fleas. A flea collar made from a piece of elastic and soaked in neat pennyroyal oil will also help. Renew the oil for both weekly.

• 30 drops of pennyroyal oil blended with 2 tablespoons of olive oil makes an excellent flea repellent lotion. Use between washes. Dab small amounts of the lotion on the animal's fur and work in with your fingers.

## FLIES

Flies are a nuisance, especially over summer, and preventive methods should become top priority. If you haven't already done so, fit insect screens on windows and doors and rubber strips on the bottom of doors to seal gaps. If you have a fireplace, block the chimney with a board that can be easily removed when next you light the fire, and keep rubbish bins tightly closed.

Check for any possible breeding areas, such as slow compost heaps, damp bedding in dog kennels, chicken pens and yards, rubbish piles, and leaking septic pipes and outlets. Encourage your neighbours to check their properties too.

Many herbs can help to deter flies, such as lavender, sweet woodruff, lemon verbena, star anise, costmary, tansy, any of the mints, thyme, rosemary, bay, chamomile, rue, elder, mugwort, southernwood and basil. Combine any of these — the more the better — in muslin or hessian bags, and hang around the house to deter flies and other insects.

Other methods of control are:

• Hang bunches of lavender, tansy and mint tied together in the kitchen, especially near doors and windows, where they will help to keep flies away.

• Rub windows and doors with a cloth soaked in either lavender oil or water which has been used to boil onions.

To make lavender oil, half fill an enamel or stainless steel pan with the dried flowers and cover them with olive oil. Bring to just below boiling, simmer for ten minutes, cook, strain and store in a dark coloured, airtight glass bottle.

- Place small dishes or saucers of fly bait in inconspicuous places around the home. The flies eat the bait and die.

To make a bait, combine ½ teaspoon of black pepper, 1 teaspoon of brown sugar, and 1 teaspoon of cream. Renew the bait every few days.
- Boil 10 g of quassia chips in 1⅔ cups (350 ml) of water for 5 minutes, remove from heat and steep for 15 minutes. Strain, sweeten with sugar and place in small dishes wherever flies gather.

## FLY TRAP

A simple trap can be made from an empty soft drink bottle. Discard the cap, then cut the top off the bottle at the shoulder, turn it upside down, insert it back into the bottle and secure with masking tape.

Drop a small piece of meat into the bottom, cover with water with a little cooking oil floating on top, attach a length of string and hang wherever flies are a problem: by the kitchen door, in attached garages or semi-open entertainment areas.

## FLY PAPER

The old-fashioned, long sticky ribbons of paper used in grandma's day are just as effective today, and are still available.

They will work just as well outside the house in an area such as an open verandah or porch. Combined with pots of fly repellent herbs like basil, lavender, peppermint, pennyroyal or fennel, fly strips will definitely help to keep the summer fly population at bay.

Alternatively, you can make your own. Commercial fly paper can be imitated by simply spreading glue on a length of yellow cardboard, approximately 30 cm long and 5 cm wide. Place a small hole in one end and attach a piece of string to hang it up.

### Fly Repellent

This is suitable for both humans and animals. Apply to pets by brushing through their hair.

*3 ml oil of cloves*
*5 ml bay tree oil*
*⅔ cup (150 ml) vodka*
*5 ml eucalyptus oil*
*¾ cup (200 ml) water*

Blend all ingredients and store in a tightly sealed, amber-coloured glass bottle. Use as required.

*See also Fruit Fly, Insect Repellents, Pets (Flies).*

## FLOORS

### CLEANING

• Wipe vinyl, ceramic and cork floor tiles over with the following herbal disinfectant cleaner.

Steep 5 tablespoons of dried lavender in a bucket of hot water until cold, strain through muslin, squeezing all liquid from the herbs, warm the water and add 2 tablespoons of methylated spirits.

• Stubborn stains can be removed from terrazzo and quarry tiles with a cut lemon dipped in salt. Rub well into the affected area, leave for 1 hour, then mop over with tepid water to which has been added 2 tablespoons of methylated spirits to every 9 litres of water.

• Grease on quarry tiles and scuff marks on vinyl can be removed with a neat soapwort decoction. Put 4 tablespoons of dried soapwort in an enamel or stainless steel pan and add enough water to cover. Bring to the boil, and gently boil for 10 minutes. Remove from heat, steep until cool, then strain through muslin.

Scrub or mop until marks disappear.

• Timber, linoleum, vinyl and cork surfaces can be polished with the following all-purpose disinfectant floor polish.

*See also Tiles.*

### Floor Polish

*1 handful eucalyptus leaves*
*4 cups (1 litre) boiling water*
*250 g soap flakes*
*150 g grated beeswax*
*4 cups (1 litre) natural turpentine*
*4 cups (1 litre) raw linseed oil*

Place the eucalyptus leaves in a ceramic bowl, add boiling water, cover, steep overnight and strain through fine muslin.

Bring the eucalyptus water to the boil, reduce to a simmer, add the soap flakes and stir until dissolved.

Melt the beeswax in a double pan over a medium heat, and when completely liquid stir in the eucalyptus water/soap mixture until well blended. Remove from heat and when cool, but still liquid, add the rest of the ingredients, beating constantly with a wooden spoon until the mixture is a creamy texture.

Store in a jar with a tight-fitting lid.

## Floor Wax Stripper

*5 tablespoons white vinegar*
*280 g bicarbonate of soda*
*1 tablespoon eucalyptus oil*
*1 tablespoon methylated spirits*
*5 tablespoons household ammonia*
*16 cups (4 litres) water*

Allow the eucalyptus oil to dissolve in the methylated spirits, then mix thoroughly with rest of the ingredients. Store in a tightly sealed, labelled bottle.

*See also Timber Stain.*

## 'FLU

*See Colds and 'Flu.*

## FOOD MOTHS AND WEEVILS

There are a large number of food moths and weevils that infect our food. Most people are familiar with weevils that spoil flour or cereal-based products, and the tell-tale webbing that betrays them.

Storing food in airtight jars is one of the best ways of preventing infestations. This can be used in combination with the following repellents:

• Try hanging small cloth sacks of black pepper in food storage cupboards.
• Dried bay leaves placed throughout storage jars, including flour and rice bins, are an effective moth repellent. Include several dried bay leaves when storing dried beans, pulses or grains.

• Place sachets of black pepper in bean and grain containers, and sprinkle a little cooking salt around shelves. Sassafras leaves can also be used.

• Put weevil repellent sachets in cupboards and amongst food. To make sachets place cloves of unpeeled garlic on a metal baking tray in a warm oven for about an hour. Combine with crushed bay leaves and add to small muslin or coarsely woven cotton bags. In large containers of food place several sachets, layering them throughout.

• Wipe all internal wood surfaces of cupboards with lavender oil — it will help to deter moths, as well as acting as a natural disinfectant.

• Put any of the citrus oils or lavender oil in a dish of water and soak large wood shavings in it. Remove and scatter amongst the cupboard shelves.

• Cottonwool balls soaked in the same oil can be popped in nooks and crannies, and amongst storage containers. Apart from their repellent action, they will leave your kitchen cupboards or pantry smelling wonderfully aromatic.

## HOUSEKEEPING

Moth repellents are only as good as your housekeeping. Therefore it is important to clean up all spilled foods, especially those that are cereal or flour-based. They could be potential breeding areas.

It is also equally important to maintain good and regular house-keeping practices:

• Keep cupboards clean, removing all foodstuffs regularly and scrubbing with soap and water.

• Dispose of all suspect food in an outside bin. Inside bins can still give the eggs a chance to hatch and infect your food.

• For bad infestations, dispose of all infected food, empty your cupboards and scrub them with soap and water, then spray with pyrethrum insecticide. Keep the room well sealed for at least 3 hours, then open it to the air for another 8 to 10 hours. Wipe all timber surfaces with lavender oil and then replace the food.

# FRAGRANT OILS

*See Air Fresheners, Bath (Aromatic and Therapeutic), Essential Oils, Furniture Polish, Incense, Stress.*

# FRUIT FLY

Fruit fly can become a serious problem in many areas, and can be devastating for the home orchard or vegetable garden, no matter how large or small.

A simple trap to control this pest can be made from empty 1¼ litre plastic soft-drink bottles. Pierce the centre third of each bottle with tiny holes (the size of a medium timber nail), add a mixture of cloudy ammonia, water and sugar to a depth of 2 cm, replace the lids and hang among fruit trees or near other plants usually affected by this pest. The mixture in the trap will attract and kill the fly.

Alternatively, add a banana peel to each bottle, and ½ cup (125 ml) water in which has been dissolved 2 teaspoons of sugar. The flies will be attracted to the stench of the fermenting fruit, find their way in and drown.

Another simple trap, using either bait, can be made from a jam jar. Simply pierce a hole about thumbnail size in its lid, add the bait and hang among trees or plants.

# FUNGICIDE

## Chamomile Fungicide

A natural fungicide can be made from chamomile flowers. It will help destroy and control damping-off fungus and powdery and downy mildew.

*1 cup (30 g) dried chamomile flowers*
*3 cups (750 ml) boiling water*

Add the herb to a non-metallic bowl, pour in boiling water, cover and steep overnight. Strain through muslin, squeezing all liquid from the herbs, and spray onto affected plants.

## Fungicide Powder

Ground mustard seeds can be used as an effective dusting powder for the control of powdery mildew.

Grind the seeds to a fine powder with a pestle and mortar, or by processing in a blender. Store in a plastic bottle with holes in its lid. Dust on affected plants as required until problem is under control.

## Seaweed Spray

A useful fungicide to help control mildew, brown rot, curly leaf and other fungi on vegetables, ornamentals and trees.

Gather sufficient seaweed to one-fifth fill a drum, rinsing away all traces of salt before using. Cover with water and allow to steep for three weeks, then dilute with two parts of fresh water. Spray onto foliage of plants. When the concentrate is exhausted the seaweed can be used as a mulch or added to the compost.

*See also First Aid (Fungal Infections), Garlic.*

# FURNITURE POLISH

All timber furniture and surfaces can be brought to a brilliant shine with easy-to-make natural polishes.

## Lemon Furniture Cream

*½ cup (125 ml) distilled water*
*1 handful dried lemon verbena*
*25 g pure soap flakes*
*125 g beeswax*
*2 cups (500 ml) natural turpentine*

In an enamel pan heat the distilled water to boiling, add the lemon verbena, remove from heat and infuse until cool. Strain and discard the herb, then add the soap flakes, stirring in well.

Melt the wax in a double pan over a medium heat and when completely liquid add the remaining ingredients, stirring until dissolved and blended. Remove from heat, pour into a ceramic bowl and beat until cool and of a creamy texture. Store in a suitable wide-mouthed container with a tight-fitting lid.

## Lemon Scented Furniture Polish

*30 g grated beeswax*
*1½ tablespoons natural turpentine*
*1 tablespoon dried lemon balm*

Reduce the herb to a powder by rubbing through a fine wire sieve.

Melt the beeswax in a double pan over a medium heat. When completely liquid, turn heat to low and add the turpentine, stirring until well blended. Remove from heat, add powdered herb and store in a wide-mouthed glass jar.

## Liquid Furniture Polish

*1½ ml lemon oil*
*1 cup (250 ml) methylated spirits*
*1 cup (250 ml) vinegar*
*2 cups (500 ml) natural turpentine*
*2 cups (500 ml) linseed oil*

Dissolve the lemon oil in the methylated spirits and then mix in all ingredients in a bottle with a tight-fitting lid. Shake well before each use.

## Spray-on Polish

A fragrant spray-on polish that is easy to make and will keep all timber surfaces shiny and clean.

*1½ ml favourite fragrant oil*
*⅔ cup (150 ml) methylated spirits*
*⅔ cup (150 ml) raw linseed oil*
*⅔ cup (150 ml) white vinegar*

Dissolve the fragrant oil in the methylated spirits, then mix together with the rest of the ingredients. Store in a pump-spray bottle and shake well before use.

Spray sparingly and use plenty of 'elbow grease' when shining.

### *Did you know ...*

the juice of the stems and leaves of lemon balm was used to give a shine to furniture? And that the juice extracted from sweet cicely seeds was once used both to polish and scent timber furniture and panelling?

# GARDEN

## NO-DIG GARDEN

This concept dates back almost 50 years and uses the layering of organic material to reduce the back-breaking work of digging. It is particularly suited to areas with poor or rocky ground.

Alternating layers of organic material are built up from ground level. They are never disturbed by any form of cultivation, but simply added to as they decompose and mulch down. Good drainage is achieved and plants generally thrive in this environment.

The first layer can consist of seaweed, kitchen scraps or leaves, and so on, on top of which is added a layer of old newspapers, then a thin layer of sawdust. Then build up with alternating layers of chicken scratch litter (if you have access to it), grass clippings, manure and compost.

Seeds or seedlings are planted in the top layer of organic matter, with watering and feeding continuing as usual. More organic material is then added each growing season.

Like all gardens, keep well mulched to conserve water and prevent evaporation, especially during summer.

## CROP ROTATION

Long before chemical fungicides and pesticides came onto the scene, gardeners prevented the build-up of pests and disease by not planting the same vegetable (or the same type of vegetable) in the same patch of soil 2 years in succession.

Instead, they rotated their crops into different beds over a 3 or 4 year period.

The following 3-year crop rotation plan is based on a vegetable patch being divided into 3 beds.

• **Bed 1** — grow all or some of these: peas, beans (bush, runner or broad), corn, silver beet, spinach and lettuce.
• **Bed 2** — cabbages, cauliflower, broccoli, turnips, radishes and kohlrabi.
• **Bed 3** — tomatoes, carrots, leeks, onions, potatoes, cucumber, celery, beetroot, zucchini and garlic.

The following year, grow the contents of bed 1 in bed 2, of 2 in 3 and of 3 in 1. Repeat the process annually.

## WATERING SEEDLINGS

Two litre plastic milk bottles make excellent watering cans, especially in garden beds where the water sits on the soil for a while before it soaks in. You can direct water to the base of young seedlings without knocking them over.

Simply pierce one or more holes in the lid, fill the bottle with water, aim at the base of the plant and squeeze.

## IMPROVING SANDY SOIL

The usual way to improve the water retention capabilities of sandy soil is to dig in plenty of compost. However, if you haven't sufficient compost available, use the following method:

Half fill a bucket with clay and add water. Once it is muddy and can be completely stirred in with the water, dilute with sufficient water so that it will flow freely through your watering can rose.

Use this liquid whenever you water your plants — it will build up the water-holding capacity of sandy soil.

## WATER CONSERVATION

• Mulch the soil surface around trees and shrubs and on garden beds — it prevents up to 73 per cent evaporation loss.
• Water the roots, not the leaves of plants. This encourages deep root growth and makes plants hardier.
• Consider sowing tougher grasses for lawns that aren't so water dependent — kikuyu, couch, Kentucky bluegrass and perennial rye.
• Soaker hoses are an efficient way to water lawns, garden beds and vegetable gardens. Low pressure, drip watering systems are ideal for country gardens where water is limited.
• Install a rain water tank to make use of roof run-off. It can be used as an efficient garden drip watering system.
• Avoid establishing garden beds at the base of trees where there will be competition for water.
• Incorporate, if possible, hedges or windbreaks to reduce the effect of the prevailing winds. This creates a micro-climate that requires less watering.

• In summer, water early morning, and in winter, or cold climates, during mid-morning.

*See also Water (Grey).*

## DRIP WATERING SYSTEM

An effective yet simple drip watering system can be made from a length of garden hose and rope. The best type of rope to use is multi-filament double braided rope, available from ship chandlers or marine suppliers. It doesn't rot, and because of its inner core, has greater sucking power than conventional rope.

Thread the rope through your length of hose, pierce holes in it at regular intervals, and then place one end in a drum of water or rainwater tank. Provided the base of your water storage tank is not at ground level, water will gradually siphon through the entire length of the rope (via capillary action) and trickle out the holes in the hose.

This is an efficient way to water at the base of plants without wasting a precious resource.

## FEEDING CITRUS TREES

To feed your citrus trees, simply dissolve a packet of washing soda in a bucket of water and pour this over each tree from the top. It will also act as a natural fungicide and curb black spot. Any leaves that are missed can be treated by dabbing the solution on with a brush.

Citrus trees and other fruit trees will benefit from composted tin cans, which return essential elements to the soil. Simply crush the cans, spread them around the tree and cover with a thick layer of mulch (about 20 cm). After approximately 12 months the cans will have completely decomposed, leaving a friable compost.

## PEST CONTROL

• Plant chrysanthemums or pyrethrum daisies in your garden as a border plant. They will keep the bugs away from your plants.
• Tie large rhubarb leaves over the tops of the cabbages and cauliflowers to protect them from insect attack.
• Grow garlic, chives and nasturtiums beneath fruit trees to act as general bug-repellents.

• To kill nematodes in the soil, drench the area with a solution made by dissolving 2 kg sugar in a bucket of water. Molasses can also be used, but not honey as it may transmit diseases to bees.

• Scale, thrips, aphids and mites can be controlled by steeping 1kg of chopped, unpeeled onions in 2 cups (500 ml) of boiling water for 60 minutes. Strain, dilute with 20 litres of water and spray every 10 days until pests are gone.

Spray late afternoon, and if required, dissolve a small amount of soft soap in the mixture so that it will adhere to plants.

• To control red spider mite, blend 2 parts of coriander oil to 100 parts of water. Shake well before use.

The oil will emulsify much more readily with the water if it can be first dissolved in a small quantity of alcohol, such as methylated spirits or vodka.

• Snails, slugs and leaf-eating insects can be discouraged in the following ways:

Create barriers for the pests using sawdust, crushed egg shells, sand or wood ash. These will deter snails and slugs, as they dislike crossing the coarse textures.

Discourage slugs by placing newspaper barriers in their paths. Fold several sheets of paper, slightly dampened, and lay in rows between young seedlings. Slugs are attracted to the paper and hide between the folded sheets. Check daily, dispose of slugs, and add paper to the compost.

Small circular rounds of mosquito netting placed over young seedlings will keep snails from them. Remove once plants are grown and established.

Make a slug and snail trap by sinking small dishes of stale beer and sweetened water in the garden at ground level.

Protect plants susceptible to moth attack with mosquito netting. Make small semi-circular frames from rigid wire and attach the netting — place over young seedlings until they are large enough to survive attack.

Join a series of these frames (hoops) together with lengths of rigid wire to form long tunnels, and again cover with mosquito netting — this is suitable for rows of young seedlings.

• Discourage birds from destroying a vegetable crop by hanging aluminium reflectors on string above the plants. Or build an old-fashioned bird scare that looks like a bird of prey indigenous to your area. Attach to a string line above the garden.

To prevent birds from damaging fruit trees, hang slices of onion or onion peelings among the fruit. Fine black thread, laced between the branches and among the foliage, is also effective.


## HERBS IN THE GARDEN

Companion planting is recognised by gardeners as an acceptable and environmentally friendly solution in controlling insect pests.

Bitter herbs such as southernwood, wormwood, rue and mugwort will not only repel slugs and insects, but can also discourage mice and birds from eating newly planted seeds. Herbs should be dried, then powdered by rubbing through a fine wire sieve. Sprinkle this powder over the garden bed and cover with a sprinkling of earth.

Mustard is also an excellent pesticide. Grow a bed of it, and when in flower cut it and dig into the ground to eliminate insect pests and their eggs. Cayenne chilli pepper, dried and powdered, can be dusted on fruit trees before the fruit ripens to discourage fruit fly. It can also be used to dust cabbages, cauliflowers, and tomato plants to kill caterpillars.

When grinding up the cayenne chilli be sure to wear rubber gloves, and do not touch your face, mouth or eyes — it burns and irritates for quite a long time.

Grind up the chillies using a pestle and mortar until reduced to a powder, and store in a suitable container with holes in its lid. Use as required.

Other herbs can be made into specific pesticides and fungicides. An all purpose concoction can be made by using equal parts of the following: spearmint (or any of the other mints), onion, garlic, hot red chillies, mustard, lavender, and rosemary. Finely chop all the ingredients, cover with water, add a pinch of yeast and leave until it all ferments. Strain off the liquid and then dilute 1 part concentrate to 4 parts soapy water and spray over any pest-infected plant.

*See also Aphids, Companion Planting, Compost, Earthworms, Fertiliser, Fruit Fly, Fungicide, Garlic, Insecticides, Mulching, Water, Weeds.*

## GARGLE

*See Colds and Flu.*

## GARLIC (*ALLIUM ASTIRUM*)

Garlic is considered to be a natural antibiotic if taken in large enough doses. It contains vitamins A, B and C, and copper, sulphur, manganese, iron and calcium, and because its oil is composed of sulphides and disulphides, garlic inactivates undesirable virulent micro-organisms in the body, without harming the helpful organisms.

When winter is just around the corner it's important to build up the body's resistance to infection. And what better and more natural way to do this than to use garlic to help boost the body's defences?

It helps to prevent colds, expel catarrh from the chest, acts as an antiseptic, will soothe a nagging cough, and relieves the symptoms of sinusitis.

If you take this on a regular basis it will cleanse choles-terol and toxins from your blood stream, aid your digestion, cleanse stale mucus from your tissues, nourish your nerves and increase your glandular secretions.

Used as an enema or internally it will kill various kinds of worms and parasites. In cases of yeast infection use garlic water as a douche, and for babies wash the affected area.

Made into an ointment it is said to bring relief to rheumatic pain and areas of muscular strain.

To sweeten the breath after taking garlic, eat a sprig of parsley.

### Garlic Ointment
Use for muscular strain and rheumatic pain.

*2 cloves garlic*
*100 g Vaseline*

Crush the cloves and mix well with the Vaseline. Store in an airtight jar.

Rub well into affected area when required.

## Garlic Cold Cure

Ideal for people who do not take garlic on a regular basis and begin to suffer from the symptoms of cold, or have a bad cold, the following garlic cure may give relief.

*2 cloves garlic, crushed*
*½ teaspoon ground ginger*
*1 tablespoon honey*
*juice 1 lemon*
*pinch cayenne pepper*
*1 cup (250 ml) boiling water*

Put all the ingredients in a prewarmed china cup. Add the boiling water and allow to steep for 10 minutes. Strain, reheat and drink immediately.

## GARLIC IN THE GARDEN

Garlic enjoys a high reputation in the garden for repelling insect pests when grown amongst other plants. Agriculturists of old used to plant garlic near their onions, cabbages and garden vegetables to keep away various flies and grubs.

Today, organic gardeners have found that highly diluted garlic extract kills or keeps away wireworm, caterpillars, weevils, black fly and aphids and other leaf-sucking insects. It is also useful against fungi such as mildew, bean rust, anthracnose, brown rot and blight.

*See also Insecticides.*

## GINGER (*ZINGIBER OFFICINALE*)

Ginger is an excellent natural antacid because it prevents the breakdown of pepsinogen to pepsin: the latter irritates tissue to cause peptic ulcers. It acts as a catalyst to the pelvic area and when taken before each meal aids in the elimination of colon gas.

Added to bathwater, either as a powder or by bruising the root, it will open the skin pores and help rid the body of waste and toxins. Add no more than the equivalent of 1 teaspoon of powdered ginger to the bath.

*See also First Aid (Travel Sickness).*

## GLASS

### CLEANING
*See Windows.*

### RECYCLING
*See Recycling.*

## GLUE

Chemical-free glue that the kids can use at home or school can be made from any tree that gives reasonable quantities of resin, and will usually be coloured according to the resin's pigment. However, a clear glue can be made from the species of wattle *Acacia senegal*. This is the gum traditionally used to make gum arabic.

Place a small blob of the gum in a piece of muslin cloth and suspend this in a small quantity of hot water until it dissolves. Any impurities will remain in the cloth, giving you a clear glue for sticking paper together. Store in a suitable container.

Alternatively, buy powdered gum arabic (from an artists' supply shop) and dissolve it in warm water until it is a thick solution.

*See also China Cement, Paste.*

## GREASE

*See Bicarbonate of Soda, Laundry.*

## GRIPE WATER FOR INFANTS

*1 teaspoon dried chamomile*
*1 cup (250 ml) boiling water*
*honey, to taste*

Put chamomile in a small enamel or stainless steel pan, add boiling water and simmer for 5 minutes. Remove from heat, allow to cool, strain, add honey and use tepid in baby's bottle.

# HAIR CARE

### HERBAL SHAMPOO

The condition of your hair is a reasonably good indication of the state of your general health. Feel just a bit off-colour and it is surprising how quickly the hair loses its sheen and body.

A good shampoo is a must for healthy hair and unlike many others, homemade shampoos contain neither synthetics nor chemicals, are completely biodegradable, and can be formulated to suit your hair type. To make your shampoo you must first prepare a base. Once made this base will keep indefinitely.

## Shampoo Base

*100 g pure soap flakes, or 100 g pure soap, finely grated*
*4 cups (1 litre) distilled water*

Simmer the water in an enamel or stainless steel pan, add the soap flakes and stir until dissolved. Alternatively, add the grated soap and bring to the boil until the soap dissolves.

Pour into a jar and store until needed.

Don't worry if the mixture gels or becomes lumpy after being left for a while, just beat it up in the blender when you make up your shampoo.

### HERBAL OILS TO USE

**Normal hair** — lavender, rosemary, lemon, geranium and carrot
**Dry hair** — lavender, rosemary, carrot, yarrow and sandalwood
**Oily hair** — rosemary, lavender, lemon, basil, sage, thyme and yarrow
**Damaged hair** — lavender, chamomile, thyme, calendula, carrot and clary-sage
**Dandruff** — rosemary, lemon, basil, thyme, lavender, peppermint and sage (thyme, rosemary and peppermint combined will not only control dandruff, but will act as a scalp and hair tonic)

### SUGGESTED SHAMPOO BLENDS

To 5 tablespoons of base shampoo add the following quantity of essential oil:

## Normal hair

*2 drops rosemary*
*4 drops lemon*
*7 drops carrot*

## Dry hair

*5 ml almond oil*
*2 drops lavender*
*5 drops carrot*
*1 drop sandalwood*

## Oily hair

*3 drops rosemary*
*1 drop basil*
*15 drops lemon*
*2 drops sage*

## Damaged hair

*5 ml almond oil*
*2 drops lavender*
*2 drops chamomile*
*3 drops calendula*

## Dandruff

*18 drops rosemary*
*10 drops thyme*
*8 drops sage*

## Scalp and hair tonic

*18 drops rosemary*
*10 drops thyme*
*3 drops peppermint*

## Instant Herbal Shampoo

A must for people when travelling. It is light to carry and easy to use, even in hard water.

Use 1 tablespoon dried chamomile for fair hair, or dried rosemary for dark hair.

*2 tablespoons dried yarrow*
*2 tablespoons dried lime flowers (optional)*
*2 tablespoons pure soap, finely grated*
*1 tablespoon bicarbonate of soda*

Finely grind all the herbs by rubbing them through a fine wire sieve and mix together with the soap flakes and bicarbonate of soda. Store in an airtight container.

Mix 1 teaspoon of the dry shampoo with a small quantity of water and massage well into scalp and hair, then rinse.

Dried herbs are available from specialty herb shops and all good health food stores.

## Dry Shampoo

When a busy schedule makes it impossible to wash your hair, a dry shampoo is the answer. In 10 minutes your hair will be clean and looking good again.

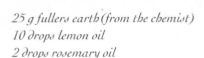

*25 g fullers earth (from the chemist)*
*10 drops lemon oil*
*2 drops rosemary oil*

Blend all the ingredients together well.

Fullers earth, if not in powder form, should be reduced to a powder with a pestle and mortar. Mix in the essential oils and then pass the powder through a fine sieve. Store in an airtight container.

To use, sprinkle a small amount over your hair and gently massage well in with your fingers. Leave for 10 minutes and then brush out using a soft-bristle brush.

## After-shampoo Rinse
To add shine to dark hair — parsley, sage or rosemary
For fair hair — chamomile, yarrow or calendula

*3 tablespoons selected dried herbs*
*8 cups (2 litres) boiling water*

Place herbs in a ceramic bowl, add boiling water, cover and steep until cool. Strain through muslin, and pour through your hair after shampooing, massaging well into the scalp.

## CONDITIONING YOUR HAIR
Continual shampooing eventually strips the natural oils from your scalp and hair. Your scalp can become dry and flaky and your hair will begin to look dull and lifeless. Essential oils help to remedy these problems.

• After shampooing, take 1 or 2 drops of either rosemary or lavender oil, or a combination of both, rub between the palms of the hands and lightly apply over your wet hair.
• A few drops of rosemary oil rubbed into the scalp after washing stimulates the blood and makes an excellent skin conditioner. Or you can add 15 drops of the oil to every 1 cup (250 ml) of your shampoo or conditioner.
• For brittle hair, mix two-thirds rosemary oil with one-third olive oil, rub between the palms and apply to wet hair.
Alternatively, pre-condition with olive oil or castor oil: rub a small quantity into the scalp and hair and wrap your head in a

warm wet towel for 30 minutes, putting a shower cap over the towel to keep the warmth in. Shampoo and give a final rinse with vinegar or lemon in the water.

## Pre-wash Conditioner

The following pre-wash conditioner has an almond oil base, which is similar to your own scalp oil. It acts as an excellent emollient that protects your skin by replacing natural surface oils, prevents roughness and chapping and nourishes your hair.

*¾ cup (200 ml) almond oil*
*2 teaspoons dried peppermint*
*2 teaspoons dried rosemary*
*1 teaspoon fennel seed*

Fill a suitable wide-mouthed jar with the almond oil and add the herbs. Seal tightly and place where it will receive plenty of hot sunlight for at least 14 days, then strain and repeat the procedure with a fresh batch of herbs. Strain the oil and store in an airtight, amber-coloured glass bottle in a cool spot.

Massage into your scalp whenever it needs extra conditioning or dry and flaky skin is evident.

If dandruff is a problem for you, replace the fennel seed with 2 teaspoons of dried thyme.

For dry hair that tangles when wet, pre-condition with a few drops of half rosemary and half lavender oil. Massage well into scalp about 30 minutes before shampooing.

## DANDRUFF CONTROL

Often food allergies and sugary diets can promote dandruff. So watch your diet and try to see if there is any correlation between what you have eaten in the last 48 hours and how bad your scalp condition is.

Rosemary or nutmeg oil massaged into the scalp can be effective. Or try the following conditioning oil:

## Conditioning Oil

*1 teaspoon dried rosemary*
*1¼ cups (300 ml) boiling water*
*30 ml almond oil*

*30 ml castor oil*
*10 drops rosemary oil*
*10 drops chamomile oil*

Put rosemary in a ceramic bowl, add boiling water, cover, steep for 12 hours, strain and blend ¾ cup (180 ml) of the infusion with the oils. Store in an old shampoo bottle.

To use, wet hair thoroughly and massage conditioning oil well into scalp and hair with fingertips for about 2 minutes. Rinse clean.

## CLEANING BRUSHES AND COMBS

Always keep brushes and combs scrupulously clean. Wash them in the following diluted rosemary decoction to eliminate any grease that has built-up.

### Brush Cleaner

*3 to 4 tablespoons fresh rosemary or 1 to 2 teaspoons dried*
*1¼ cups (300 ml) distilled water*

To make a decoction, add rosemary to an enamel or stainless steel pan containing distilled water. Bring to the boil and then gently boil for 15 minutes. Remove from heat, cover the pan, and allow to steep until cool. Strain through muslin cloth, squeezing all liquid from the herbs.

Store in the refrigerator and dilute 1:1 before use. You can extend the life of the rosemary water by adding 2 teaspoons of vodka to every 1¼ to 2 cups (300 to 500 ml) of decoction.

*See also Aloe Vera, Rosemary.*

## HANDS

Hands suffer harsh treatment from the rigours of day-to-day living, and therefore deserve special attention. Natural protection with softeners and moisturisers will keep them supple and looking beautiful.

### Protective Hand Cream

Working in the garden can be rough on the hands. To protect them you need an effective, natural barrier cream that will help to prevent skin from cracking and splitting.

Not only will the following cream protect hands from rough work, it will also protect them from drying detergents and grime. Smooth it into hands before gardening or immersing them in washing water.

*40 ml lemongrass infusion*
*25 g anhydrous lanolin*
*10 g beeswax*
*75 ml almond oil*
*2 teaspoons lemon juice*
*3 drops friars balsam, from the chemist*

Prepare the infusion by adding a handful of the lemongrass to a ceramic bowl and covering with just sufficient boiling water. Steep for 2 hours and strain.

Melt the lanolin and beeswax in a double pan over a medium heat. When liquid, add the almond oil and lemongrass infusion, stirring until well blended. Remove from heat, allow to cool, add lemon juice and tincture of benzoin and beat until cold and creamy.

Store in a sterilised glass jar.

## Herbal Hand Cleaner

This cleanser has the ability to remove ingrained dirt and stains from the hands.

*equal quantities of dried sage and dried yarrow*
*30 ml olive oil*
*20 ml almond oil*
*sugar*

Finely grind the herbs by rubbing them through a fine wire sieve and mix them together. Mix 1 teaspoon of the blended herbs and sufficient quantity of sugar with the oils to form a paste. Store the cleanser in a wide-mouthed jar with a tight-fitting lid.

Rub dirty hands with the paste until they are free of stains.

## Lemon Hand Cream

Use this natural moisturiser to keep your hands supple and

to help prevent skin from cracking or splitting, and to restore the skin's acid balance.

Apply after using the Herbal Hand Cleaner or whenever required.

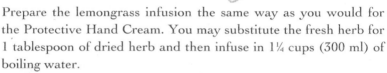

*40 ml lemongrass infusion*
*10 g beeswax*
*5 g anhydrous lanolin*
*40 ml almond oil*
*35 ml castor oil*
*2 teaspoons lemon juice*
*3 drops friars balsam, from the chemist*

Prepare the lemongrass infusion the same way as you would for the Protective Hand Cream. You may substitute the fresh herb for 1 tablespoon of dried herb and then infuse in 1¼ cups (300 ml) of boiling water.

Melt the wax and lanolin in a double pan over a medium heat. When liquid stir in warmed oils, lemongrass infusion and lemon juice. Remove from heat, add tincture of benzoin, and beat continually until cool and of a creamy texture.

Store in a sterilised glass jar.

### Tomato Hand Lotion
Mix equal parts of tomato juice, lemon juice and glycerine. Massage well into hands and wrists. This will cleanse as well as soften them.

### Rosewater Lotion
Mix equal parts of lemon juice, rosewater and glycerine. This lotion will not only clean and nourish the hands, but will also strengthen the fingernails.

### Honey and Almond Night Oil
A rich, oily overnight conditioner for hands that have been excessively exposed to harsh climatic conditions. Massage well into hands, then wear cotton gloves for increased absorption.

*1 teaspoon honey*
*1 tablespoon almond oil*

*1 tablespoon olive oil*
*½ tablespoon glycerine*

Gently warm the honey and oils in a double pan until they are well blended. Remove from heat and beat in the glycerine.

Bottle and seal.

*See also Fingernails.*

## HAYFEVER

*See Sinusitis.*

## HEADACHE

Causes of headaches are numerous, but whatever the cause it is usually associated with a great deal of discomfort. There are a number of simple remedies you may wish to try next time a headache persists.

• Minor headaches can be relieved by putting a couple of drops of lavender oil on your fingers and massaging your temples. For tension headaches put a few drops of lavender oil in a bowl of warm water, wring out a handkerchief in it and apply to the back of the neck.

• A tea made from the herb meadowsweet will ease a nagging headache. Aspirin is found in this plant.

### Meadowsweet Tea

To make a tea infuse the herb in the following proportions:

*1 tablespoon fresh meadowsweet or 1 level teaspoon dried herb*
*to 1¼ cups (300 ml) boiling water*

For individual cups, pour in hot water, cover, infuse for 3 minutes, and strain into another cup.

If brewing in a teapot, allow 1 serve per individual and one for the pot. Infuse for 5 minutes in boiling water, then strain into individual cups. Use only a ceramic teapot as metal or aluminium may contaminate your herbal tea.

• For general head pain, add 1 drop each of fennel, lavender, peppermint, rosemary and sage oil to a bowl of hot water. Place your face about 30 cm above the bowl and cover your head with a towel so as to form a tent, and to prevent vapour from escaping. Inhale the steam, but for no longer than 10 minutes.

*For migraine headaches see Feverfew.*

*See also Chamomile, First Aid, Pain, Vinegar (Herbal).*

## HEATING

### MAKING THE MOST OF WINTER SUN

Turn a north-facing (south-facing in the northern hemisphere) window easily and simply into an effective greenhouse to make the most of winter sun. As well as providing additional warmth, it can be used to grow herbs, flowers and even year round tomatoes. Add adjustable shelves to provide extra space for all your potted plants, and a hanging rod at the top to dry clothing.

Your window greenhouse should extend approximately 60 cm from the windowsill and can be framed and entirely glazed or made from an old window sash. If the unit fits under the eave, flashing may not be needed. Otherwise, use a suitable waterproof material, such as galvanised tin plate — available from most hardware stores. Seal fixing screws or holes with a waterproof sealer.

A sun trap will also bring added warmth to your home, and save on energy. Sun traps absorb the warmth of winter sun during the day and then re-radiate the heat at night.

This can also be achieved by surrounding your house with large dark pots or sand-filled tubs. Or place them inside the house in front of a north (south in northern hemisphere) window.

## HERBS

### AIR DRYING

This requires no special arrangements: simply tie the herbs and flowers in bunches and hang them upside down in a dry, airy, shady place, or spread them out thinly on net-covered trays and keep in a warm, well-ventilated place. Usually, herbs will take 4 to 12 days to dry, sometimes longer.

- Leaves are dry when brittle, but will not shatter.
- Flowers are ready when petals feel dry and slightly crisp.

- Roots should be dried right through with a soft centre.
- Seeds, after being removed from seed-heads, should be placed in the sun for a few hours.

## OVEN DRYING

This is a less satisfactory method since temperatures must be maintained below 32°C. Spread the herbs on trays and leave the oven door ajar to ensure ventilation.

## MICROWAVE OVEN DRYING

Most herbs, especially parsley, which does not respond well to air drying, can be dried successfully in a microwave oven. It is advisable to do a few trial runs first to determine the best drying times. Turn the oven on to full power and lay the washed herb on 2 layers of absorbent paper on top of an ovenproof tray. Usually it should take no longer than 4 minutes to dry each batch. Herbs with delicate, feathery leaves such as fennel and dill weed, do not respond to this type of drying technique.

## STORING DRIED HERBS

When dry, herbs should be rubbed gently by hand to discard the hard stalks — not too finely or they will lose their fragrance — and stored in clean airtight containers. If you are storing them in metal bins, first put them in a linen or cotton bag. All containers should be kept in a cool, dark place so that the herbs will keep their fragrance.

The following should be observed when storing herbs:

- Thyme, sage and rosemary can be left on the stalk.
- Seeds and flower-heads should be placed immediately into airtight containers.
- Roots should be ground like coffee beans in a grinder or blender, and only stored in airtight glass containers.

If at any time the container shows signs of moisture on its inside, the herbs weren't correctly dried. Remove the herbs and place them on a sheet of plain paper and allow further drying time.

At the most, dried herbs will only last for a year, so always remember to replace them. An accurate way to check is to put the date on all your containers.

## FREEZING HERBS

Herbs to be frozen should be picked with long stems so that you can tie them into bunches. Put together a convenient number of sprigs, either the same or mixed, whatever you will need to use later, and tie, leaving a long thread. Wash quickly and lightly, and shake off the excess water. Plunge the herbs into boiling water and hold there for 1 minute, then dip them into iced water for 2 minutes. Drain very well — they must be quite dry before freezing.

Place each bunch into a square of plastic or a tiny plastic bag, tie the top and pack in labelled boxes. If required chopped, do it while they are frozen just before using them.

To use, drop the frozen herbs into soups, stews, etc. Chives and basil do not need to be blanched, before being frozen.

### Green Herbal Drink

As well as being highly nutritious and cleansing, this herbal drink is excellent for people suffering bad breath. Make fresh each day and take morning and night as required.

*250 g mixed wild herbs — chickweed, Fat Hen, dandelion*
*2 tablespoons finely chopped parsley and/or watercress or celery*
*1 teaspoon cider vinegar*
*1 small carrot, chopped*
*250 g chopped fruit (apple, peaches, pineapple or watermelon)*
*1 cup (250 ml) liquid to dilute (orange juice, pineapple juice, vegetable broth or mineral water)*

Select combination, process in blender and serve immediately.

*See also Garden, Hair Care, Hands, Lavender, Oregano, Pets (Herbs), Potpourri, Rosemary, Teas (Herbal), Teeth (Mouthwash), Vinegar (Herbal).*

## HERBAL FIRST AID

*See First Aid.*

## HERBAL TEAS

*See Teas (Herbal).*

## HORSERADISH

*For Horseradish Chest Rub, see Colds and Flu.*

# INCENSE

For hundred of years herbs and spices have been used to cover up and eliminate offensive odours in the home. Burning scents like frankincense and myrrh dates back to the ancient Egyptians, and continued through the centuries with sweet spices like cinnamon, quassia, cloves, allspice and nutmeg being included.

Burning herbs and spices still has a place in the home: not to mask staleness and bad odours as they did in those dank houses of the past, but to perfume the air with an enjoyable sweetness.

## Homemade Incense

*1 tablespoon very fine sawdust*
*1 tablespoon spice or dried, ground herbs (reduce herb to powder by rubbing through a fine wire sieve)*
*1 teaspoon gum arabic*

Thoroughly mix the sawdust with the spice or herb, then add 1 tablespoon of water in which the gum arabic has been dissolved. When all the ingredients are mixed together, shape into cones and allow to dry.

Place cones on small metal dishes, or other suitable objects, and light — the incense will smoulder, filling the room with fragrance.

For more exotic smells, or an aroma that's a little mysterious, experiment with your own blends by mixing different spices and herbs. Or you might like to try the following mixture. Use 1 tablespoon of this in the Homemade Incense in place of the spice or dried, ground herbs.

## Spice Mixture for Incense

*equal quantities of the following:*
*freshly crushed cinnamon*
*crushed allspice*
*crushed nutmeg*
*minced vanilla pod*
*powdered dried lemon peel*

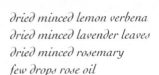

*dried minced lemon verbena*
*dried minced lavender leaves*
*dried minced rosemary*
*few drops rose oil*

Blend ingredients and add the rose oil a drop at a time until sufficiently scented, but not so that it is overpowering.

### Lavender Incense Sticks
This incense is made from the flower-head stalks.

*1 tablespoon saltpetre*
*1 cup (250 ml) warm water*
*dried lavender stems*

Dissolve the saltpetre (available from the chemist) in the warm water and soak the lavender stems in it for 30 minutes. Dry out and light for a slow smouldering scent.

Experiment with other herb stems, using only the wood on which the new season's growth appears.

*See also Air Fresheners.*

## INDIGESTION

*See Essential Oils.*

## INK STAINS

Remove with a citric acid solution or lemon juice and salt and then wash.

Milk will remove ink stains from linen and calico if applied immediately. Soak the affected area in milk for a few minutes, then wash in clean water.

To remove an ink stain on carpet, immediately cover with salt to absorb the stain. Remove salt by vacuuming or brush off with a stiff broom.

*See also Ballpoint Ink, Lemon.*

## INSECT BITES AND STINGS

Washing stings in vinegar as soon as possible relieves pain, as will a slice of fresh onion placed on a wasp or bee sting.

Insect bite itch can be relieved by applying cornflower infusion generously to the affected area, or rubbing with bruised rosemary, lemon balm, basil, sage or plantain leaves. Apply Calendula Ointment as needed.

*See First Aid.*

*See also Ants (Bites), Itching, Juniper, Mites, Spider Bite.*

## INSECTICIDES (GARDEN)

### Rhubarb Spray

Rhubarb can be made into a liquid insecticide that will destroy aphids and most other leaf-sucking insects. This spray is extremely poisonous so take great care with its storage and use.

*1½ kg rhubarb leaves*
*12 cups (3 litres) water*
*120 g soft soap (from the chemist)*

Boil leaves in water for 30 minutes. Do not inhale the fumes while the mixture is boiling. Strain, mix with soft soap and spray on affected plants.

Rinse edible plants thoroughly before you include them in food.

### Garlic Spray

Garlic insecticide will kill and keep away wireworm, caterpillars, weevils, black fly and aphids and other leaf-sucking insects. It is also useful against fungi such as mildew, bean rust, anthracnose, brown rot and blight.

*1 cup (160 g) crushed garlic*
*2½ tablespoons mineral oil*
*10 g soft soap*
*4 cups (1 litre) warm water*

In an airtight jar soak the crushed garlic in mineral oil for 2 days. Dissolve the soft soap in warm water and mix with garlic and oil, strain, and then dilute one part concentrate with 49 parts water.

Spray as required.

### Feverfew Spray

This is a broad spectrum spray that can be used to control a wide range of garden pests.

Like all organic sprays it breaks down quickly; so if you spray one day and have pests a week later, don't blame the feverfew. It would have killed them, it's just that more pests would have moved in.

*4 tablespoons feverfew flowers*
*4 cups (1 litre) hot, soapy water*

Steep the flowers in hot, soapy water for 1 hour, then strain. Cool before using. Spray at night outdoors so that it doesn't affect bees and other useful insects, and only in conjunction with other preventive measures.

## Quassia Insecticide
A mild, but quite effective spray for controlling garden pests such as aphids, mealybugs, etc. Spray late afternoon so as to not affect ladybirds and bees.

*30 g quassia chips*
*4 cups (1 litre) water*
*20 g soft soap*

Bring quassia chips to the boil in water, and then reduce to a simmer for 30 minutes. Remove from heat, strain and mix in soft soap. Dilute 1 part concentrate with 3 parts water.

Quassia spray is a safe, natural insecticide that breaks down within 24 hours, leaving no harmful residue.

## All-purpose Insecticide

*3 chilli peppers*
*½ onion*
*1 clove garlic*
*water*

Blend chopped chilli peppers, sliced onion and garlic in water. Boil, steep for 2 days and strain. This spray will not damage indoor or outdoor plants and can be frozen for future use.

Before using, mix in a little soft soap so that it adheres to the plants.

*See also Ants, Aphids, Cockroaches, Fruit Fly, Garden (Herbs in the Garden, Pest Control).*

# INSECT REPELLENTS

There are many natural, organic personal repellents which you can use to make outdoor activities pest-free and more enjoyable.

Flies, mosquitoes, midges and sandflies are all repelled by lavender oil. It can be applied neat to exposed skin, if you avoid contact with eyes and mouth. Dab on a few drops and massage well into the skin — renew every couple of hours. Other oils which will also repel insects are, in order of their effectiveness, eucalyptus, paperbark, Huon pine, grey myrtle and citronella.

You can dilute any of these oils with an odourless vegetable oil, provided it remains highly fragrant, to make it spread further. Or alternatively you can blend your own personal repellent to have handy whenever you're out of doors or insect pests are a problem.

## Lavender Repellent

*6 drops lavender oil*
*5 ml vodka*
*⅔ cup (150 ml) warm water*

Dissolve the lavender oil in the vodka and then mix with the warm water. Bottle and use as required.

## All-purpose Repellent

*5 ml oil of cloves*
*5 ml lavender oil*
*5 ml eucalyptus oil*
*⅔ cup (150 ml) perfumer's alcohol or vodka*
*¾ cup (200 ml) distilled water*

Dissolve the essential oils with alcohol, then mix well with the distilled water. Store in an airtight glass bottle and use as required, applying liberally to the skin.

## Quassia Repellent

Steep a handful of quassia chips in a bowl of cold water for 24 hours. Strain and bottle.

Sponge the liquid onto skin whenever mosquitoes are a problem.

Try the chemist, health food store or herb specialty shop for quassia chips.

## NIGHT-TIME PESTS

On warm summer evenings during outdoor activities, to keep pests away you have the following choices: personal repellents, an insect repellent light, or repellent candles. Choose any of the previous recipes for a suitable body repellent.

In outdoor entertainment areas install red lights where you eat and cook, as they will help to repel insect pests; a white light some way off will attract pests. Avoid zappers, they will also kill large numbers of beneficial insects.

Burning eucalyptus leaves in the barbecue will repel mosquitoes, flies, gnats and midges. A far simpler solution is to burn insect repellent candles, such as citronella.

## REPELLENT CANDLES

Eucalyptus or citronella candles burning in a room will help to repel mosquitoes and blowflies, as well as making the room smell clean and fresh.

Beeswax makes the best candles, but can be expensive unless you can purchase it direct from a beekeeper. If you don't have access to a cheap source, use solidified paraffin wax available from some supermarkets or hobby shops.

For moulds you can use empty drink cans, milk cartons, toilet rolls, yoghurt containers, and so on. Wicks can be bought from hobby suppliers or craft shops. Or you can use No. 4 knitting cotton.

Melt the wax in a double pan over a medium heat so that it does not burn. When completely liquid add 20 ml of eucalyptus or citronella oil to every 2 cups (500 ml) of wax.

Attach one end of the wick to a piece of blu-tack, position in the centre of the bottom of the mould, secure the other end to a pencil laid across the top. Pour in the liquid wax and allow to harden — 3 to 4 hours — before using. Trim the wick to 1 cm, remove the candle from the mould and discard the blu-tack.

When using moulds, such as toilet rolls, tape a circular cardboard disc to the bottom.

Other fragrant or repellent oils can also be used in making candles.

*See also Clothes Moths, Fleas, Flies, Food Moths and Weevils, Garlic (In the Garden), Mosquitoes, Silverfish, Ticks.*

## INSOMNIA

All of us at some time have one of those nights where we toss and turn and just can't sleep. Fatigue, tension, anxiety, overexcitement or pain are some of the causes of an occasional sleepless night.

If you have had a hectic day, relax at night and avoid evening activities that are mentally demanding. Don't bring your work home from the office. Drink a cup of chamomile tea instead of coffee after dinner and another cup half an hour before going to bed. If you're really wound up, relax in a soothing and calming warm herbal bath.

Herbs you can use in the bath are bay leaf, chamomile, hyssop, lemon balm, lime (linden) flowers, lovage, pennyroyal, rosemary, valerian and yarrow. Put 2 tablespoons of dried herbs of your choice in the centre of a 20 cm square of muslin. Draw up the sides and secure them with a piece of ribbon then hang them under the running tap so that the water gushes through it.

However, if you continually suffer from insomnia, your diet may be inadequate and you may not be getting sufficient vitamins and minerals to soothe jangled nerves and tone up the nervous system. Check your calcium and magnesium intake, and if required take a daily supplement, available from your health food store. Valerian tea, an hour before going to bed, can help to re-establish a normal sleep cycle, and can be safely taken in conjunction with any prescribed medication. Because of valerian's off-putting taste, it can be blended with equal amounts of a better-tasting herb such as mint. You can also add honey to taste, if required.

*See also Bath, Lavender, Teas (Herbal).*

## IRON

### Cleaning

• Clean the inside of an iron by filling with equal parts vinegar and water. Allow to steam a minute or so, switch off and leave for an hour. Wash out with clean water.

• Clean the face by applying bicarbonate of soda with a damp cloth, gently scrubbing until clean.

• Remove starch from the face by sprinkling salt on a sheet of brown paper and moving the warm iron over it a few times.

## Lavender Ironing Spray

Spray on clothes when ironing for a fresh, soft scent.

*4 teaspoons dried lavender*
*2 cups (500 ml) boiling water*
*10 ml vodka*

Steep lavender in boiling water until cold. Strain through muslin, squeezing all liquid from the herb, add vodka and drip through filter paper.

Store in a pump-spray bottle and use as required on a fine mist setting.

## ITCHING

### Peppermint Bath

A peppermint tea bath is very soothing for itches.

*4 teaspoons dried peppermint*
*2 cups (500 ml) boiling water*

Put the dried peppermint in a ceramic bowl, add boiling water, cover and steep until cool. Strain through muslin cloth and add to bath water.

### Marigold Lotion

Apply marigold lotion as a soothing balm.

*2 tablespoons dried marigold (calendula) petals*
*5 tablespoons glycerine*

Put ingredients in a small ceramic bowl in a pan of boiling water. Simmer over a low heat for 30 minutes. Remove, strain, and discard used petals. Store in a sterilised glass bottle with a tight-fitting lid.

Apply generously to affected area as needed.

*See also Insect Bites and Stings, Mites.*

### Did you know ...

that chickweed and olive oil will soothe itchy rashes? Simply simmer 1 cup of chickweed in ½ cup (125 ml) of olive oil for 30 minutes. Cool, strain and apply to affected area as required.

Keep surplus lotion in a sterilised glass bottle for future use.

## JOJOBA

Jojoba (pronounced ho-ho-ba) is a traditional healing plant. The golden oil, or wax, extracted from its seed pod has many uses as a cosmetic oil and its excellent lubricating qualities make it a fine moisturiser for the skin. Included in homemade moisturising creams it will not only moisturise, but help to soften the skin, leaving it with a smooth, silky texture.

It can be used to treat such conditions as dry scalp, psoriasis and eczema. Jojoba also conditions the hair and it is a familiar ingredient in many commercial soaps and shampoos.

### PRACTICAL APPLICATION

• Apply a few drops directly onto chapped or sore lips, dry skin or general skin disorders like eczema, psoriasis, dandruff or acne.
• Use it to treat persistent warts — add a drop of oil to the affected spot morning and evening.
• Eat a few ground and roasted jojoba beans each morning to strengthen a weak stomach and relieve acidity; but don't take excessive amounts. Large quantities may have a purgative effect.
• Because jojoba contains anti-inflammatory myristic acid it also has potential value to relieve rheumatism and arthritis. Rub the oil directly into sore joints whenever required.

### Jojoba Moisturising Cream

*10 g beeswax*
*5 g wool fat*
*50 ml jojoba oil*
*20 ml almond oil*
*5 ml wheatgerm oil*
*20 ml aloe vera juice*
*20 ml distilled water*
*6 drops friars balsam, from the chemist*

Melt the beeswax and wool fat in a double enamel or stainless steel pan over a medium heat. When completely liquid add warmed oils, aloe vera juice and distilled water, stirring until well blended. Remove from heat, pour into a ceramic bowl, add tincture of

benzoin and beat until cool and of a creamy texture. Store in a sterilised glass jar with a tight-fitting lid.

Apply a little to face or hands morning and night, massaging gently into the skin.

## ST JOHN'S WORT

*Did you know ...*

in medieval times a childless wife would plant St John's Wort — when the herb flowered, would walk naked at midnight through her garden and pick the flowers. It was believed that this would enable her to have a child by the time of the next St. John's Eve.

## JUNIPER

A small evergreen tree which, since ancient times, has been accredited with having mystical properties. The ripe berries can be made into a tea that cleanses the body, and is reputed to restore vigour. They are particularly useful in all urinary problems, and are one of the best diuretics known. Externally the tea can be used to soothe insect bites and bee stings. (WARNING: Overuse of the tea can inflame the kidneys.)

Juniper oil added to the bath, or used as an inhalation, is refreshing, stimulating and invigorating. It can be used in an aromatherapy massage, therapeutic foot bath or aromatic shower.

### Juniper Bath Oil

*80 ml soapwort liquid*
*40 ml almond oil*
*10 drops juniper oil*
*10 drops rosemary oil*
*10 drops pine oil*

To make the soapwort liquid: Put 40 g dried soapwort in an enamel or stainless steel pan, add 2½ cups (600 ml) of water, bring to the boil and allow to boil for 5 minutes. Remove from heat, cover and steep until cold. Strain through muslin, squeezing all liquid from the herb. Store for future use.

Add ½ cup of this liquid to the bath water to give it a gentle, cleansing effect that leaves the skin feeling smooth and soft.

To make the bath oil: Pour the almond oil and essential oils in a jar, seal and shake to mix. Place the jar in a pan with about 5 cm of water and simmer for an hour. Mix in the soapwort liquid and beat well. Store in a suitable bottle and add 1 tablespoon to your bath when you feel like relaxing. The fragrances will soothe away nervous tensions.

## KAOLIN

Kaolin (China clay), a very fine clay used in ceramics, can be used as a natural base for a facial mask.

Mix together ½ cup (125 ml) each of kaolin and plain yoghurt with ½ teaspoon of honey to form a paste. Apply to face and neck, avoiding the eyes, leave on for 10 minutes, then rinse off and moisturise the skin.

It will leave your skin feeling smooth and refreshed. You can also add 2 drops of any of the following essential oils for added effect.

- **To stimulate:** lavender, lemon and rosemary
- **To purify and destroy bacteria:** sandalwood and peppermint
- **For a calming effect:** chamomile
- **To calm and soothe:** almond and jasmine
  Kaolin is available from your local chemist.

## KETTLES AND ELECTRIC JUGS

To remove 'fur' in a kettle, half fill with potato peelings and top up with water. Boil for 1 hour, topping up with hot water if necessary, empty and rinse thoroughly.

To clean plastic electric jugs or kettles, add 1 cup (250 ml) of white vinegar, top up with water, boil for 10 minutes, and rinse out well.

## KITCHEN

### KITCHEN ODOURS

- To get rid of cooking odours and other nasty kitchen smells, burn a few sprigs of southernwood on a little metal dish.
- To eliminate cooking odours, put 1 cup (250 ml) of rosemary vinegar, or other herbal vinegar (*see Vinegar (Herbal)*), close to the stove.

- Deodorise your refrigerator after cleaning by placing an open packet of bicarbonate of soda inside it. This will keep it smelling fresh for up to 3 months.
- Place a sprig of rosemary or any other savoury herb in the oven whenever you bake; its fragrance will soon fill the kitchen.
- Rub mustard into hands to remove the smell of fish.
- Remove onion odour from hands by rubbing with salt.
- To deodorise jars and bottles, pour in a solution of water and dry mustard and allow to stand for several hours.
- Eliminate odours from wooden cutting boards by rubbing them over with salt. Wipe clean with cold water and then rub over again with a handful of fresh spearmint or peppermint to leave them smelling fresh and clean.
- Deodorise bread boxes or bins by wiping over with 3 tablespoons of bicarbonate of soda dissolved in 4 cups (1 litre) of warm water, or a herb vinegar such as rosemary or thyme.

*See also Air Fresheners.*

## HERB BAGS

Herb bags are little sachets made from scraps of leftover coarse material, such as hessian, gathered across the top and tied with a ribbon. They can be filled with fragrant herbs to combat cooking smells, freshen up a broom cupboard, and eliminate mustiness from a duster and odds-and-ends drawer.

Hang them around the room, over the backs of chairs and in cupboards, squeezing them whenever you walk past to release their scent.

## Lemon Delight

*75 g dried lemon verbena*
*25 g dried lemon-scented geranium leaves*
*25 g dried peppermint*
*2 pieces dried lemon peel, powdered*
*2 tablespoons orrisroot powder*

In a large ceramic bowl mix all the ingredients thoroughly, using your hands. Place the mixture in an airtight plastic bag and seal tightly. Leave in a dry, cool, dark spot for 6 weeks, and give the contents a good shake every other day.

## KITCHEN DRAINS
*See Bicarbonate of Soda.*

## ALL-PURPOSE CLEANSER
*See Bathroom.*

*See also Cleaning, Cooking, Dishwashing, Disinfectant, Oven, Pastry Boards, Recycling (Kitchen Scraps), Saucepans.*

# KITCHEN CURES

Some of the fruit and vegetables we use almost daily in the kitchen have natural curative properties. This is no doubt the reason they have been used continually over the centuries as both a food source and natural medicine, although today their benefits are not very widely known.

So next time you're feeling a little out of sorts, check out your refrigerator and pantry — a remedy may be closer than you think.

## APPLES
Without doubt there is no better remedy than grated raw apple for general stomach upset and gastric disturbances. It is especially good when taken after diarrhoea, as it will quickly restore the bowel function to normal.

## BANANAS
When you're feeling tired and in need of a quick energy fix, try a banana. Mashed and mixed with a little honey and avocado, and served on oat biscuits, it makes a powerful energy-packed snack.

The inside of a freshly-peeled banana skin is an excellent first aid dressing for cuts, abrasions and small wounds and burns. Bind loosely with a bandage, renewing every 3 hours until it is relieved.

## BARLEY
Barley has long been known to have an anti-inflammatory action on the genito-urinary tract. To help reduce the discomfort of cystitis try some old-fashioned barley water. Simmer 50 grams of unrefined barley (from the health food

shop) in 4 cups (1 litre) of water for 40 minutes. Cool, strain and drink over 24 hours.

## BEETROOT

The juice of raw beetroot is also a natural remedy for cystitis, as well as for constipation, anaemia and skin diseases. Drink a glassful morning and night.

## BRAN

Taken internally, it is an excellent remedy when recovering from an illness where there are signs of mineral deficiency, such as from skin diseases.

Add 2 tablespoons of bran to a pan and pour 2 cups (500 ml) of boiling water over it. Bring to the boil and simmer over a low heat for about 15 minutes, cook, and strain. Take a cupful 3 to 5 times daily, as required.

Externally, it can be used as a poultice for muscle and joint complaints. Pour 2 cups (500 ml) of boiling water over 2 table-spoons of bran. Mix well and apply warm in a cloth bag.

## CABBAGE LEAVES

*See Aches and Pains, First Aid, Pain.*

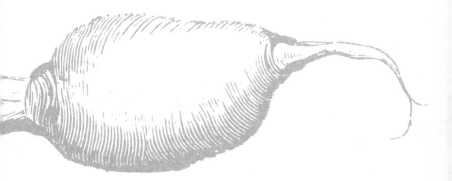

## LABELS

To remove sticky marks left by adhesive labels and price tags on most surfaces (glass, vinyl, leather, laminex, wood) wipe the surface gently with methylated spirits and a few drops of eucalyptus oil.

Adhesive labels and tape can be removed from vinyl surfaces, without leaving a mark, by moistening well with eucalyptus oil. Leave for several minutes and lift off. You may need to repeat this a few times — then wipe over with methylated spirits and eucalyptus oil.

## LAMINEX

Laminex bench tops and other surfaces can be cleaned with a paste of bicarbonate of soda and vinegar. Apply with a non-metallic scourer and wipe off with a damp cloth.

## LAUNDRY

There are many environmentally safe laundry products available from your local supermarket, all of which are clearly marked and in most instances expensive to buy. It is just as easy to make your own products at home from cheap, easy to obtain ingredients.

*See also Cleaning, Soap.*

### Laundry Gel

*50 g pure soap, grated*
*¼ cup (60 g) washing soda or bicarbonate of soda*
*16 cups (4 litres) water*

Add the grated soap to a saucepan half filled with water, stir over a medium heat until boiling, then turn down to simmer. Whisk or mash to completely dissolve the soap. Add either the washing soda or bicarbonate of soda (these act as a water softener), remove from heat and add to a bucket containing 16 cups (4 litres) water, stirring until well blended.

The mixture will set into a soft gel and may be stored. One or two cups of gel in a full washing load should be sufficient.

If you wish to give your wash a soft fragrance, infuse herbs such as lavender, lemon verbena or rose petals in the 4 litres of water first. Simply add 4 tablespoons of dried herb to a bucket, cover with boiling water, steep overnight and strain through muslin. Then add required amount to the recipe.

## PRE-WASH PROCEDURE

Before switching from detergent to a pure soap-based product, put your laundry through a cycle of washing soda. This will remove the traces of detergents left in your clothes and prevent them from yellowing when you change to the gel.

Dissolve 250 grams of washing soda in 9 cups (2¼ litres) of hot water, and add 2 cups (500 ml) of this solution to every full load. Use in moderation, as indiscriminate use of washing soda may cause damage to delicate fabrics, giving an unacceptable result.

### Eucalyptus Wash Mix

This mix is excellent for washing away dirt from all garments, and especially grease from overalls.

*450 g pure soap, grated*
*50 g purified borax*
*3 tablespoons methylated spirits*
*1 tablespoon eucalyptus oil*

Blend soap and borax together in a double boiler over a gentle heat, stirring constantly. Pour into a suitable mould, such as a small wooden box lined with damp calico, and allow to cool and harden.

Reduce again to flakes — running the soap over an inverted carpenter's plane is the quickest and easiest way of doing this.

Add the soap and methylated spirits to a large jar and stand overnight, then add eucalyptus oil. Store until needed, giving a good shake before use.

You should use 1 tablespoon of the mixture for every 36 cups (9 litres) of water.

### Eucalyptus Wool Mix

Use this for washing all your woollens, including that favourite jumper. It will also provide protection against moths and silverfish.

*4 cups (360 g) pure soap flakes*
*2 cups (500 ml) methylated spirits*
*1 tablespoon eucalyptus oil*

Mix soap flakes with methylated spirits and eucalyptus oil. Store in an airtight bottle.

For a jumper, use about 1 tablespoon of the mixture in a basin, and proportionately more in the washing machine. Dissolve the mixture in hot water, then add cold water to correct temperature. Do not rinse out as the eucalyptus oil provides protection against insect damage.

### Herbal Fabric Wash

Use for washing delicate fabrics and lingerie.

*1 cup (145 g) finely ground bran*
*4 tablespoons dried soapwort*
*2 teaspoons dried lavender*
*4 cups (1 litre) distilled water*

Boil the bran, soapwort and lavender together in an enamel or stainless steel pan for 20 minutes. Strain through muslin, squeezing all liquid from the ingredients, and dilute as required.

Wash garment by hand in the solution, then rinse.

### Fragrant Rinse

Keep your clothes smelling fragrant and fresh by adding 1 to 2 cups of lavender water to the final rinse of your washing machine.

*4 teaspoons dried lavender*
*2 cups (500 ml) boiling water*

Steep lavender in boiling water. When cool, strain through muslin, squeezing all liquid from the herb. Add to your wash.

### Moth Repellent Rinse

Use at the end of winter to provide protection for blankets and precious woollens that are to be stored away.

Add an infusion of the following herbs to the final washing rinse or, if washing by hand, rinse well in clean water and then a final rinse of the infusion.

*4 teaspoons dried lavender*
*2 teaspoons dried rosemary*
*2 teaspoons dried wormwood*
*2 cups (500 ml) water*

Steep herbs in boiling water. When cool, strain through muslin, squeezing all liquid from the herbs. Add to wash.

## SOFTENING WATER
When you want to add a water softener to your clothes washing water, simply add a handful of washing soda or bicarbonate of soda. They are both environmentally friendly, safe, cheap and will do the same job as expensive chemical softeners.

## LAVENDER IRONING SPRAY
*See Iron.*

## DRY CLEANING WOOLLEN GARMENTS
Woollen garments, including cream-coloured jumpers, can be dry cleaned by heating a mixture of 1 tablespoon each of flour and salt in the oven until fairly hot. Rub this mixture on the soiled areas of the garment, then fold it over and leave for 24 hours. Shake to remove dry cleaning paste.

## MILDEW
To remove mildew from a garment sponge with lemon juice and then place in the sun until all the mildew spores are gone. Delicate fabrics and woollens should then be washed in Herbal Fabric Wash.

## PERSPIRATION
To remove perspiration stains from woollen jumpers, sponge the area with white vinegar, then wash in warm salty water. If the stains are old and stubborn apply a paste made from 1 tablespoon cream of tartar, 3 crushed aspirins and warm water. Just leave to dry, and then rinse thoroughly.

To remove perspiration stains from other fabrics, soak garments in a solution of 2 tablespoons bicarbonate of soda and 18 cups (4½ litres) of cold water. Leave for 1 hour before washing. Old stains can be sponged with vinegar before washing.

## STAINS

Bicarbonate of soda is a mild alkali, useful for neutralising acid stains. Soak stained fabric in warm water containing 2 teaspoons of bicarbonate of soda, leave for 1 hour, then rinse well. Grease can be removed by pouring hot water on stains and covering with dry bicarbonate of soda.

For cocoa and chocolate milk stains on clothes, sponge with cold water, then rub with glycerine and leave for half an hour. Then wash with soap and water and rinse.

To remove coffee stains, mix an egg yolk with lukewarm water and rub onto the stain, then wash as normal.

To remove coffee from woollens, mix 2 teaspoons of glycerine, 1 teaspoon cloudy ammonia and 4½ tablespoons of water, and apply to the stain, rubbing gently. This mixture can be stored in a tightly sealed bottle for future use.

Curry stains can be removed by soaking the stain with methylated spirits, then washing.

To remove tea stains from clothing, first sponge the spot with cold water, then rub with glycerine. Leave for 30 minutes, then wash with soap and water and rinse.

To remove marks made by dead matches, rub clothing or material which has been marked with a piece of cut lemon, and then with a cloth dipped in water.

*See also Wax.*

## SOILED NAPPIES

Presoak soiled nappies in 45 g bicarbonate of soda dissolved in warm water, wash in hot soapy water and then dry.

# LAVENDER

The English word 'lavender' originated from the Latin verb *lavo*, 'I wash', and for centuries lavender has been used for soaps, in bath water and to add a clean, fresh scent to bed linen and clothes.

There are a number of different varieties of lavender, the best known being the English lavenders (*Lavandula angustifolia* and *Lavandula spica*) and French lavender (*Lavandula dentata*), which has a slightly less potent perfume.

All lavenders are native to the Mediterranean region but have now been introduced to many parts of the world. They will grow in full sun in temperate climates, but may need protection in warmer climates.

The dried flowers are used in potpourri and herb sachets, and the essential oil can be included in natural cosmetic preparations and ointments. It has a mild tranquilising effect, which you can experience by merely picking the flower buds and inhaling their scent. The oil calms the nerves and relaxes tension and is used in aromatherapy to ease headaches and relax the body. As a herbal vinegar it will refresh a sick room and protect against bacteria.

## PRACTICAL APPLICATIONS

• Unwind with a mixture of 3 drops lavender oil and 3 drops rosewood oil in your evening bath.
• Lavender oil rubbed into the wrists or onto the nape of the neck has a calming effect.
• Use the oil as a cleanser for your face. Mix one drop of oil to 5 tablespoons of distilled water and apply with a cotton ball.
• To clear blemished skin, mix 2 drops each of lavender oil and chamomile oil in the palms of your hands, then massage into facial skin each evening after thoroughly cleansing. Leave on overnight.
• If a blemish is coming up, dab on 1 drop of lavender oil to help it disappear.
• Individual sores or insect bites can be dabbed directly with lavender oil.
• If you suffer from insomnia, put one drop of lavender oil on your pillow and you'll be asleep in minutes.

### Lavender Ointment

An excellent cream for burns, chapped lips, cold sores and so on.

*10 g beeswax*
*5 g cocoa butter*
*65 ml almond oil*
*10 ml wheatgerm oil*
*40 ml aloe vera juice*
*15 drops lavender oil*
*15 drops sandalwood oil*

Melt the beeswax and cocoa butter in a double boiler over a medium heat. When the mixture is completely liquid add the warmed almond and wheatgerm oils and aloe vera juice, stirring until well blended. Remove from the heat, pour into a ceramic bowl, add the essential oils and beat until cool and creamy. Store in a sterilised glass jar with a tight-fitting lid. This will keep for 6 to 12 months.

*See also, Bath (Sachets), Essential Oils, Food Moths and Weevils, Insect Repellent, Iron (Spray), Oven, Vinegar, Windows.*

## LEATHER

To preserve leather furniture and shoes and to prevent cracking apply the following polish.

### Rejuvenating Polish

*2¼ cups (550 ml) raw linseed oil*
*1 cup (250 ml) white vinegar*

Bring linseed oil to the boil over a medium heat, remove from heat source, allow to cool, and mix thoroughly with the vinegar. Store in a tightly sealed bottle until needed.

Apply the oil with a soft cloth, rubbing it well into the leather. Keep changing to a clean area of the cloth as you go. When you have put the oil all over the leather, get another soft, clean cloth and rub the leather with this until it shines.

*See also Shoes, Upholstery.*

# LEMON

The humble lemon has many practical uses, from deodorising a room to cleaning and removing stains. Plant one in your garden if you have space. The best varieties are Lisbon, Meyer or Eureka.

Lisbon will produce large fruit with an abundance of juice. Meyer is useful for tub growing on a patio or home unit balcony. It is less acid than other lemons, resists frost better and is therefore suitable for growing in colder districts. Eureka bears better in summer, giving good quality juicy fruit. So, whatever you need, there is a lemon tree to suit you.

## Try Using a Lemon!

• A few slices of lemon placed in a shallow dish of water will remove the smell of cigarette smoke from a room.

• For a room deodoriser, mix the juice of 1 lemon with 4 cups (1 litre) of strong tea. Strain and store in a pump-spray bottle. Spray into rooms to make them smell fresh. Do not spray onto furniture or carpet, as it can stain.

• Ink and mildew stains may be taken out of white clothes by rubbing with lemon and salt and then washing. Rust stains can be removed from cotton garments with a mixture of lemon juice, salt and borax.

• A few drops of lemon juice added to dishwashing water will make glass shine and remove stains from porcelain.

• 3 or 4 drops of lemon juice makes an excellent substitute for shining leather shoes.

• Deodorise your refrigerator or garbage bin by washing it out with 4 cups (1 litre) of water to which has been added 1 teaspoon of lemon juice.

*See also Ants, Brass, Copper, Marble, Oven (Microwave).*

# LICE

## Quassia Rinse
An old-fashioned treatment for head lice is a rinse made from

quassia chips. The quassia (pronounced Kwarsha) is a small South American tree that has natural insecticidal qualities. *See Quassia.*

*15 g quassia chips*
*8 cups (2 litres) water*
*cider vinegar*

Boil the chips in the water in an enamel or stainless steel pan for 2 hours. Strain and add 1 tablespoon of cider vinegar to every 1¼ cups (300 ml) of liquid.

Apply by combing through the hair with a very fine comb. Repeat at two week intervals, 3 times.

Quassia chips were once available from the chemist, or you can try your local health food store or herb shop.

## Essential Oil Treatment

*25 drops rosemary oil*
*25 drops lavender oil*
*13 drops geranium (pelargonium)*
*75 ml almond oil*
*12 drops eucalyptus oil*

Mix the oils together well. Divide the hair into small sections and saturate each section with mixture down to the roots. Pile long hair on top of the head ensuring that every bit is oiled. Wrap plastic around the head and behind the ears to stop the oils from evaporating. (Be careful with small children that they cannot move the plastic anywhere near their noses or mouths and restrict their breathing.) Leave on for 2 hours, remove and shampoo, rubbing in well. Rinse thoroughly and comb through with a fine comb. Repeat 3 days later.

## LIPS

### Honey and Rosewater Lip Salve
An excellent healing cream for sore, dry lips that have been exposed to the extremes of winter cold and winds.

*1 tablespoon honey*
*1 teaspoon rosewater*

Gently melt the honey in one bowl sitting in another bowl of hot water, and stir in the rosewater. Bottle and seal, and use as required.

## Moisturising Lip Gloss

Lips look and feel at their best when they are soft and smooth. A moisturising and medicated lip gloss will not only keep your lips moist and supple, but will also soothe and repair them.

*15 g beeswax*
*15 g anhydrous lanolin*
*40 ml wheatgerm oil*
*20 ml apricot oil*
*20 ml almond oil*
*40 ml distilled water*

Melt the wax and lanolin in a double pan over a medium heat, add the oils and water and stir until well blended. Remove from the heat and beat until it is cool and of a creamy texture. Store in a sterilised glass jar.

Apply as needed.

# LIPSTICK

To remove lipstick stains from clothing sponge with glycerine, leave for 30 minutes, sponge with eucalyptus oil, then wash in warm soapy water.

# LOOFAH

An alternative to buying and using synthetic dishwashing sponges is to grow your own. A vegetable sponge, better known as a loofah (*Luffa aegyptiaca*), is a gourd that can be used, when dried, as a dishcloth, for scrubbing pots and pans, for wiping up spills, or for washing yourself in the bath or shower.

Loofah gourds are grown like zucchinis and are a quick growing annual that is more easily managed if given something to climb on, such as a back fence or trellis. When immature, under 15 cm long, they can be picked and eaten as a vegetable, tasting a little like zucchini or okra.

The fruit is ready to harvest for sponge making when the stalk shrivels. Cut off the end, remove the seeds and hang in a sheltered spot, such as a verandah, so that the gourd will dry naturally in the sun. The fruit will turn yellow and wither and the skin will then flake off leaving the sponge-like fibres. Soak the sponge in clean water overnight, wash thoroughly in hot, soapy water, rinse clean, dry in the sun and it is ready for use.

Discarded sponges can be added to the compost, and if you have a bumper crop each year, barter excess sponges with neighbours or give them away as gifts.

Specialist herb nurseries or garden suppliers may carry *Luffa aegyptiaca* seeds.

## LOVAGE

*Did you know ...*

that lovage is one of the best bath herbs? Added as an infusion it cleanses, deodorises and heals, and has natural relaxing and rejuvenating properties.

As a cold tea it is excellent as a gargle for throat and mouth infections, or a soothing lotion for tired and sore eyes.

## MAKE-UP REMOVER

*1 teaspoon dried mixed herbs (sage and yarrow)*
*15 g beeswax*
*25 ml avocado oil*
*40 ml jojoba oil*
*10 ml eucalyptus oil*
*5 ml wheatgerm oil*
*20 ml aloe vera juice*

Finely grind the dry herbs to a powder and mix together. Melt the beeswax in a double boiler over a medium heat and add the oils and aloe vera juice, stirring until well blended.

Remove the mixture from the heat and pour into a ceramic bowl. Beat the mixture continually until it cools. Store it in a sterilised, screwtop jar.

Massage a small amount lightly into facial skin and then wipe off with a soft, clean cloth.

## MALVA

*Did you know ...*

that malva, a common roadside weed, contains up to 17 per cent of essential minerals and has one of the highest vitamin A counts of any herb?

Combined with marshmallow, another wild herb, it makes an excellent treatment for teenage acne.

## MARBLE

To clean marble flour boards or other surfaces, first sponge off with clean water, then dissolve salt in lemon juice and rub on with a clean cloth.

## MICE

*See Rodents.*

## MICROWAVE OVEN

*See Oven.*

# MIGRAINE

See Feverfew, Headache.

# MILDEW

See Laundry.

# MILK SUBSTITUTES

See Dietary Substitutes.

# MIRRORS

## To Clean
See Windows.

## Prevent Steaming Up
Rubbing with a cloth moistened with glycerine will prevent mirrors from steaming up while showering. Rubbing with soap and then polishing with a clean cloth will also work.

# MITES

Usually, mites are too small to be seen with the naked eye, and when an infestation occurs it can be a continual source of irritation, resulting in a rash or even dermatitis.

Most mites can be washed off with some very hot soapy water. First, soak in a hot bath to which you have added 10 ml each of eucalyptus and lavender oil. Scrub yourself thoroughly with a bristly brush, then take a long hot shower immediately after your bath.

If the mites don't respond to the soap and water treatment, it would be wise to seek professional help to determine exactly what sort of mite infestation you have.

Other precautions to take are to air carpets, mats, cushions, and lounge covers for several days or place them in a plastic bag, to which has been added a few sprigs of lavender, and place outside in the sun, or have them dry cleaned. Do likewise with bed linen after thoroughly vacuuming.

## MOISTURISER

### FACE
*See Skin Care.*

### HANDS
*See Hands.*

## MORNING SICKNESS

Any of the following herbal teas are beneficial: wild raspberry leaf, lemon balm, cinnamon, alfalfa. Drink a cup 3 times every day. However, raspberry leaf tea, if taken in excess, can bring on uterine contractions. It is therefore not recommended for use in the last three months of pregnancy.

A drop of spearmint oil on your pillow at night is also beneficial.

*See also Essential Oils (Indigestions and Nausea).*

## MOSQUITOES

Screens fitted to doors and windows are one of the best controls to prevent entry to your home. In areas where mosquitoes are in plague proportions it may also be wise to sleep under mosquito netting.

However, cleaning up breeding areas is first and foremost. Get rid of stagnant water — dog dishes that are topped up instead of emptied, tins and bottles, tubs, buckets around the yard, old tyres — anything that can hold water.

If it is necessary to have containers around the yard, cover them with screen wire or add some vegetable oil to them (this will form a thin film on top, preventing mosquitoes from breeding). And if you live in a rural area, don't forget your rainwater tanks — they can become a breeding haven.

Keep goldfish in outdoor ponds — they love mosquito larvae. Permanent water, such as creeks and dams, also make ideal breeding places. Stock them with fish suitable to your area. Contact your local office of the Department of Agriculture and Fisheries for information.

Grow willows, casuarinas or melaleucas in wet, boggy areas to drain surplus water. Install drains.

## REPELLENTS

• Burn eucalyptus, citronella or lavender candles, or the essential oil in a simmering pot, inside or at night around the barbecue or outdoor entertainment areas.

• Save prunings from your herb plants, especially lavender, and throw them on your barbecue fire. Pennyroyal will also work, as well as green eucalyptus leaves. The latter, however, should only be used as a last resort, since it makes a very smoky fire.

• Burning lavender incense sticks inside and outside is another very effective repellent.

• Body repellents are also a must when outdoors, and the following oils, in order of their effectiveness, can be used: lavender, eucalyptus, paperbark, grey myrtle, citronella, pennyroyal.

To make a repellent, blend 6 to 10 drops of the oil of your choice with 5 ml of vodka and then mix with ½ cup (125 ml) of warm water. Apply immediately, then every 2 hours for women and every 4 hours for men.

## PLANTS THAT REPEL

Grow cedronella (*Cedronella tryphylla*) throughout the garden, near entrance doors or around outdoor entertainment areas. It can be sown directly in the soil or grown in pots.

Cedronella is a herbaceous bush with ferny lemon-scented leaves and pink to violet flowers. It is an excellent mosquito repellent and will also repel other insects. Either grow it from seed or purchase established plants from your local nursery.

Other plants that will repel are castor-oil plants and citronella-scented geraniums (pelargoniums).

### Mosquito Spray

This will both kill and repel mosquitoes and breaks down quickly to leave no residue.

*1 cup (100 g) fresh wormwood leaves, tightly packed*
*water and methylated spirits*

Infuse the herb in just sufficient boiling water to cover for 12 hours. Strain through muslin, squeezing all liquid from the herb, and then dilute 1 part infusion to 4 parts water. Add 2 teaspoons of methylated spirits to every 2 cups (500 ml) of liquid.

Store in a pump-spray bottle and use on a fine mist setting.
*See also Insect Repellents.*

## MOTHS

*See Clothes Moths, Food Moths and Weevils.*

## MOULD

*See Bathroom.*

## MOUTHWASH

*See Aloe Vera, Teeth.*

## MUGWORT

*Did you know ...*

that mugwort oil (St John's plant: *Artemisia vulgaris*) was once used in magic as a love divining herb and in dream pillows to make your dreams interesting?

Today it is used as a bath oil: a few drops added to bath water are good for colds, bronchitis, rheumatism, fever and headaches.

## MULCHING

Mulching your garden with organic matter is one of the best and most efficient ways of keeping soil and plants healthy and happy. It generally improves soil texture as well as providing a number of other benefits:

• It prevents weeds from emerging in the soil between rows and around the base of plants.
• It reduces the need for excessive watering by keeping the soil moist and prevents loss of moisture through evaporation.
• A steady supply of nutrients is supplied to the plant roots.
• Soil texture is improved because it is kept lightly moist.
• Decaying mulch builds the soil into rich, friable humus.

Apply the mulch as previous applications break down, maintaining a good deep layer. However, be sure that the mulch is not placed too close to the base of newly planted seedlings.

## MATERIALS SUITABLE FOR MULCHING

• Mushroom compost, if a source is handy.

• Homemade compost is suitable for all soil types and conditions.

• Manure — cow or horse manure is the best choice and should be pulverised before applying to the soil. This can be done by running the lawnmower over it a few times until sufficiently broken down. Well rotted poultry manure can also be used and should be mixed with some type of fibrous litter. Its high nitrogen content is excellent for promoting leaf growth in vegetables such as silver beet and lettuce.

• Grass clippings — use as a top layer mulch only unless combined with manure or compost.

• Pine bark chips — make an excellent top layer mulch or can be used in combination with manure or compost.

• Leaf mould or mulch — can only be used after it has become well rotted. Either add in layers to the compost or rake up leaves into a pile in autumn, water well and allow to break down into a friable mulch.

*See also Compost, Garden.*

## NAIL CARE

*See Fingernails.*

## NAPPIES

*See Laundry.*

## NASTURTIUM

*Did you know ...*

that a tea made from either the flowers, leaves or seed of the nasturtium plant is excellent as a bronchial medicine when the phlegm contains hard yellow lumps?

## NETTLE (*URTICA DIOICA*)

### Nettle Fertiliser

A nitrogen-rich garden fertiliser that will make plants thrive.

Rot a large quantity of nettles in a drum filled with water. Leave for 2 weeks and then dilute 1 part concentrate with 10 parts water. Use as a liquid plant food every 2 weeks during growing season.

## NEWSPAPERS

*See Recycling.*

## NITS

*See Lice.*

## NUTMEG OIL

*Did you know ...*

that for digestive problems 2 drops of nutmeg oil can be taken in honey after each meal?

## ODOURS

*See Air Fresheners, Incense, Kitchen, Laundry (Fragrant Rinse), Lemon, Shoes, Urine.*

## OIL

If you service your own car at home one of the problems you'll be faced with is what to do with the used sump oil.

Engine oil can be recycled by simply cleaning it through a homemade capillary system. For this you will need 2 containers and several lengths of plastic tubing and rope. The most effective rope is multi-filament double braided, and is available from most ship chandlers. It has an inner core and outer covering, giving it greater sucking power.

Place one container, full of dirty oil, on a bench and the collection container below the level of its base. Thread a suitable length of rope through a piece of plastic tubing and then place one end in the top container, approximately 3 cm from its base, and the other end just hanging in the top of the lower container. The oil will slowly siphon down the rope, cleansing the oil of foreign bodies.

Several lengths of rope will speed up the process.

Carry out this procedure a number of times using clean containers and siphon ropes until all traces of detergent have been removed, and the oil has regained its viscosity. The oil can now be reused.

Multi-filament double braided rope does not rot so it can be continually used for this purpose. Occasionally, however, it might need to be cleaned by soaking it in kerosene and then allowing it to dry before future use.

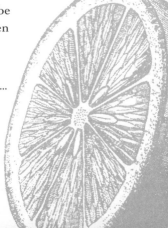

## OILS, ESSENTIAL

*See Essential Oils.*

## ORANGE OIL

*See Skin Care.*

## OREGANO (*ORIGANUM VULGARE*)

Oregano grows well in most areas of Australia and is commonly used as a border plant or in rockeries.

Taken as a tea it expels flatulence, induces perspiration, eases cramps and griping pains, and relieves painful menstruation. When the oil is rubbed into the abdomen it will give relief to menstrual pain and cramping of the organs. The essential oil can be used as a rub in the treatment of bruises, sprains and muscular pain.

## OVEN

There is no need to resort to harmful chemicals or throw your arms up in despair next time the oven needs cleaning. A paste of bicarbonate of soda and water will not only effectively do the job, but is guaranteed not to harm you or the environment.

Mix sufficient bicarbonate of soda and water to form a stiff paste and spread it over the inside of the oven, then heat for 30 minutes. When the oven has cooled brush the bicarbonate of soda off — it will remove all traces of burnt fat and grease.

To loosen foods that have become baked on, place 4 tablespoons of bicarbonate of soda in the bottom of an enamel, ovenproof glass or ceramic baking dish and add just enough water to cover the bottom of the dish. Heat the oven for 30 minutes, switch off, and leave the dish of bicarbonate of soda in overnight.

### OVEN DOOR

To clean the glass on an oven door wipe over with a clean cloth dipped in bicarbonate of soda, then sponge off with clean water. The glass can then be wiped over with the following lavender cleaner, to give it a fragrant, sparkling clean shine.

### Lavender Cleaner

*3 teaspoons dried lavender*
*2 cups (500 ml) boiling water*
*8 drops lavender oil*
*2 teaspoons methylated spirits*

Place the lavender in a ceramic bowl, add boiling water, cover, steep overnight, and strain through fine muslin. Dissolve the lavender oil in the methylated spirits, blend with the herbal infusion and drip through filter paper. Store in a pump-spray bottle.

Apply with a damp cloth, then buff off with wads of newspaper.

## OUTSIDE THE OVEN

Wipe the outside and around hot plates with the following:

### Disinfectant Cleansing Liquid

*4 tablespoons dried soapwort*
*2 tablespoons dried lavender*
*30 drops lavender oil*
*2 tablespoons methylated spirits*
*clean water*

Place the herbs in an enamel or stainless steel pan and cover with 1½ cups (375 ml) of water. Bring to the boil, then reduce to a simmer for 30 minutes. Remove from heat, cover and allow to infuse until cold. Strain through fine muslin, squeezing all liquid from the herbs, and top up with clean water to make 8 cups (2 litres).

Dissolve the lavender oil in the methylated spirits and mix thoroughly with the herbal water. Store in a pump-spray bottle for future use.

For hard-to-remove burnt on grime, apply a paste of bicarbonate of soda, leave on for 15 minutes, wipe off and then apply the Disinfectant Cleansing Liquid. In nearly all circumstances the natural cleanser will remove even the most stubborn stains.

## MICROWAVE OVENS

Microwave ovens can be cleaned by wiping over with the Disinfectant Cleansing Liquid.

To eliminate cooking odours, combine 1 cup (250 ml) of water with the juice of ½ lemon, lemon rinds and 5 whole cloves. Place in a suitable container and put into the oven on HIGH for 3 to 5 minutes.

## PAIN

The following kitchen herbal remedies are safe, mild treatments for the relief of pain, and are suitable for children.

For infant teething, digestive pain, mild colic and wind, disturbed sleep, irritability:

Steep 1 or 2 chamomile teabags (from the health food shop) in a cup of hot water, plus a little powdered ginger root to taste. Strain, and give 1 teaspoon frequently.

### INFANTILE COLIC (GAS AND FLATULENCE)

1 teaspoon each of caraway seed, anise seed, fennel seed and basil. Bruise the seeds and mix ingredients in 1 cup (250 ml) of boiling water. Cool, strain, and give frequently by the teaspoon.

More serious pain: nausea, cramps and spasms, vomiting and diarrhoea.

Mix the following freshly powdered spices thoroughly in 1 cup (250 ml) of boiling water: 1 teaspoon cinnamon, ½ teaspoon cardamom and ¼ teaspoon nutmeg. Strain the mixture, and sip while hot, or give by the teaspoon.

### HEAD PAIN

Blend equal parts of the following essential oils: fennel, lavender, peppermint, rosemary and sage. Add 6 drops of oil to a bowl containing 1¼ cups (300 ml) of hot water, place your face about 30 cm above bowl and cover your head with a towel to form a tent. Inhale the steam for no longer than 10 minutes.

*See also Headache.*

### TOOTHACHE

*See First Aid.*

## EARACHE

*See First Aid.*
*See also Aches and Pains, Kitchen Cures.*

## PAINT

### Hardy Paint

A simple-to-make paint that will withstand rain and other weather conditions without coming off. It can be used on external surfaces, including galvanised iron.

*3 kg tallow*
*3 kg dry, powdered lime*

Place the tallow in a large bucket so that it completely covers its base, add the lime and then enough water to cover the ingredients by approximately 10 cm. When the heat from the lime has melted the tallow, stir the mixture thoroughly until the ingredients have dissolved and are well blended. Store in a container with a tightly fitting lid.

Apply to dry surfaces with a large, wide brush.

This paint will dry to an off-white and can be coloured by the addition of powdered earth pigments, such as red iron oxide, chrome oxide, cobalt, yellow ochre, burnt umber, etc. To obtain the desired colour shade, first experiment with a small quantity of paint, then add the oxide/s proportionately to the balance.

### GLOSS PAINT

To render the basic paint more durable for timber surfaces, and to give it a bright gloss, add 2 cups (500 ml) of milk to every 18 cups (4½ litres) of paint just prior to application.

### CRACK FILLER

A filler for fine cracks can be made by mixing a little flour with some of the paint to form a soft putty. Rub into cracks just prior to painting and gently wipe off any surplus.

## PAINT ODOUR

The smell of fresh paint can be removed by placing half a raw onion in a bowl of water in the middle of the room.

*See also Timber Stain.*

## PAPER

*See Recycling, Xmas.*

## PASTE

This is an old-fashioned recipe for making paste and can be used for scrap books, gluing cardboard and papier-mâché modelling.

Simply add sufficient water to a cup of flour to make a thick paste. Don't keep any longer than a week.

*See also Glue.*

## PASTRY BOARDS

To clean, scrape off leftover dough, sprinkle with salt and rub with a slightly dampened cloth or sponge.

## PEPPERMINT

*Did you know ...*

that many kinds of indigestion can be alleviated by a dose of 3 drops of peppermint oil, taken either on a sugar cube, as a tea, or in hot water, after each meal ?

## PERSPIRATION

*See Laundry.*

## PESTICIDES

*See Insecticides.*

## PETS

### HERBS FOR PETS

In the wild, animals seek out and chew their own remedies, and indeed cats and dogs often nibble grass or other plants. However, now that they live in our environment, those plants which help to keep them well are not always readily available.

You can add these herbs as supplements to their diet as well as using them to treat simple ailments. And if they are introduced at an early age, you'll find your pet will enjoy them.

Include garlic, parsley, watercress and dandelions finely chopped or minced, and combined with some grated raw carrot. To this add wheatgerm flakes, yeast, cod-liver oil and kelp. Mix ingredients thoroughly with raw meat.

Vary the diet by just including some or all of the ingredients.

Caged birds will appreciate fresh dandelion leaves, chickweed or grass seed heads. Cats enjoy catmint. Also, catmint included in a sachet with dried wormwood and placed in the pet's bed will repel fleas. A sachet of dried rue or pennyroyal in the dog's basket also helps to keep fleas at bay. You can rub dried wormwood leaves into the cat's coat and tansy leaves into the dog's as extra flea deterrents. Brush the herbs out well after a few minutes.

In the aviary, plant a southernwood bush to help prevent bird lice, and if you have a fish pond add some chopped up parsley once a week to the water. Fish love it.

*See also Dog Washing Soap.*

## HERBAL FIRST AID

The following remedies are only for simple complaints and problems. Any serious ailment should be referred imme-diately to your veterinarian.

All herbal infusions in the following remedies are formulated on the following proportions, and steeped in boiling water until cool. Add 2 teaspoons of dried herb to a ceramic bowl and pour in 1¼ cups (300 ml) boiling water. Strain before use.

## ABSCESS

Put 1 drop of tea tree oil on the affected area. Once the pus has discharged, apply 1 drop of lavender oil and then clean with salt water.

## ANAL SWELLING

Dilute 5 drops each of chamomile oil and tea tree oil in 5 ml of olive oil, and apply to the area with cottonwool.

## BAD BREATH

Add 1 drop of aniseed oil to each feed. Wash the gums and teeth with rosemary infusion using a toothbrush. Also administer a cupful of the infusion each day. If the cause is gingivitis, blend 1 drop each of clove, lavender and myrrh oils with a teaspoon of olive oil and apply to the gums with a toothbrush.

## BALDNESS

Loss of hair not caused through disease may be treated by adding dandelion leaves to your pet's daily meal. Also rub the affected spots with a mixture of 5 drops eucalyptus oil dissolved in 1½ tablespoons castor oil. If the complaint persists, see your local vet.

## BRONCHITIS

Apply a warm cloth, on which have been placed 2 drops each of eucalyptus and neroli oils, to the back and chest .

## BURNS AND SCALDS

Cold water followed by neat lavender oil, as soon as possible.

## COAT

If your pet's coat is in poor condition, try this treatment. Blend 5 drops each of carrot oil and evening primrose oil with 1 tablespoon each of olive oil and wheatgerm oil. Store in an amber-coloured glass bottle, in a cool spot, for up to 2 months.

Add ¼ teaspoon of the mixture to each meal.

## COLDS AND 'FLU

This can be a common complaint in some dogs, and can be treated with the following rub: dissolve 2 drops each of tea tree oil and eucalyptus oil in 1½ tablespoons of olive oil. Apply to the chest, all around the rib cage, around the throat and, most importantly, in a direct line from the ears into the shoulders.

For long-haired dogs, or for people who don't like putting oil on their pet's coat, blend 2 drops of either tea tree or eucalyptus oil with 1 teaspoon of vodka then dissolve this with 1½ tablespoons of water. Apply as before.

You should also treat the area where your pet sleeps with the following spray to get rid of the bacteria and viruses lurking there. Dissolve 6 drops each of eucalyptus and lavender oil in 1 teaspoon of methylated spirits and mix with 2 cups (500 ml) of water in a pump-spray bottle.

## CUTS AND ABRASIONS

Bathe the affected area with an antiseptic, made by adding 6 drops of lavender oil to a bowl of warm water.

## COUGHS

Minor, persistent coughs can be treated by giving your dog or cat an infusion of equal parts elderflower, thyme and horehound.

Administer a cup of infusion mixed with a little honey 2 to 3 times daily.

## CYSTS

Apply 1 neat drop of lavender oil.

## EARS

Foreign bodies can be removed by carefully adding 1 teaspoon of olive oil. Later, dry out with swabs and diluted witch-hazel (from the chemist).

Canker, which is common in long-eared dogs, can be treated by cleansing the affected ear daily with 3 parts rosemary infusion and 1 part witch-hazel.

Ear wax is, unfortunately, a common problem in dogs and can become smelly and offensive. It needs to be removed and then the ear should be deodorised and disinfected.

Dilute 3 drops of lavender oil in 5 ml of witch-hazel solution and insert at least 4 drops in each ear. Gently massage the whole ear and repeat this procedure daily to soften the wax. It can then be removed with cottonwool.

## FLEAS

*See Fleas.*

## FLIES

Odour is the usual cause of flies being attracted to a pet. Check its state of health: diet, eczema, overactive scent glands, infection and sores from scratching fleas, and so on.

Mix 1 teaspoon of eucalyptus oil to every 1¼ cups (300 ml) of warm water and comb this through the animal's fur. Serious complaints, or those from no obvious cause, should be referred to the vet.

*See also Flies.*

## LOSS OF APPETITE

Usually, the best treatment for an animal that doesn't want to eat is to feed it nothing for two to three days except for a little grated raw apple. You can also try giving it a cup of peppermint infusion twice a day.

## MANGE

Good food rich in vitamins A and B for prevention — herbs such as garlic, parsley, watercress and dandelions finely minced and combined with some grated raw carrot. To this add wheatgerm flakes, yeast, cod-liver oil and kelp.

Treat by clipping fur away from the affected area and then bathing with warm soapy water to which has been added a few drops of olive oil.

## RHEUMATISM

Dissolve 5 drops each of ginger oil and chamomile oil, and 2 drops of rosemary oil in 1½ tablespoons of olive oil and massage into the affected area.

## TICKS

*See Ticks.*

## TRAVEL SICKNESS

For dogs who travel in the family car, valerian is one of the most powerful herbal sedatives and tranquillisers. The chopped roots can be given to pets in their normal food prior to a journey, and will relax them without sedating them. 2 tablespoons of fresh root should be enough for a large dog.

## VOMITING

Administer 2 tablespoons of herbal tea, made from equal parts peppermint, rosemary and thyme, 3 times daily.

## WORMS

Usually worms are the result of a bad diet; they love fats, sugars, eggs and milk. A well balanced diet should prevent them from becoming a problem. A natural preventive is to include 2 teaspoons of any of the following foods in your pet's diet each day: grated raw carrot, ground raw pumpkin seeds, finely chopped garlic, melon or grapes.

*See also Dog Washing Soap.*

# PLASTIC

*See Recycling.*

# POLISH

*See Brass, Copper, Floors (Polish), Furniture Polish, Leather, Shoes.*

# POSSUMS

### Quassia Spray

To deter possums, spray quassia wherever they are a nuisance. The smell will keep them away.

*30 g quassia chips*
*4 cups (1 litre) water*
*20 g soft soap*

Bring the quassia chips and water to the boil and then simmer for 30 minutes. Remove from heat, strain and mix in the soft soap until completely dissolved. Dilute 1 part mixture with 3 parts water and use as required.

# POTS

*See Saucepans.*

## QUARRY TILES

*See Floors.*

## QUASSIA (*QUASSIA AMARA*)

The quassias (pronounced Kwarsha) are native to South America and Jamaica. The chips, or wood shavings, taken from these trees were once used for the eradication of head and pubic lice.

It has natural insecticidal qualities which made it ideal for controlling many soft-bodied insects. A strong infusion of the wood shavings can be used to spray fruit to repel birds, or to deter possums. It is also used as a fly bait and to repel mosquitoes.

The principal constituent of quassia is quassin, which has a very bitter taste, and when used in an infusion a strong, bitter odour. It is this bitterness that gives quassia its repellent qualities.

Quassia chips used to be available from the chemist and you may still find this a ready source. Health food stores and specialty herb shops may also have them. If you do have trouble locating them, they may be purchased by mail order from the following:

The Fragrant Garden, Portsmouth Road, Erina, NSW 2250
Tel 043 677322
Univas, Units 6–8, 13–14 Works Place, Milperra, NSW, 2214
Tel 02 773 0100
Phoenix Seeds, PO Box 207, Snug, Tasmania, 7054
Tel: 002 67 9663

*See also Fleas, Insecticides, Insect Repellents, Lice, Possums.*

## RADIATOR

*See Car Radiator.*

## RATS

*See Rodents.*

## RECYCLING

Lots of bottles, containers, newspapers, and other miscellaneous items can be recycled at home. Here are a few ideas to put these 'throwaways' to good use.

### CANS

• Large fruit juice cans make excellent bulk storage containers in the home workshop, or use them for plant pots — paint them a suitable colour and make sure 4 medium-size holes have been drilled in the bottom to allow air to the roots and water to run through.

• Brightly painted tins of various sizes, with press-down lids, make inexpensive, yet attractive kitchen canisters.

• A large can that has the top and bottom cut out, when placed around young trees, will give support and protection until they have established themselves.

• There are dozens of other uses for empty tins, all that is required is a little imagination. Once you've run out of ideas and uses, simply compost them.

*See Compost.*

### CEREAL PACKETS

When spring approaches it's time to think about a head start on the season and begin propagating your vegetable seedlings.

Cut used cardboard cereal packets into cylinders and secure with masking tape for excellent propagators.

Fill cylinders with soil, plant a seed in each one and stand them in an empty ice-cream or other suitable container. When seedlings are large enough, plant them out, cardboard cylinder and all.

Old cardboard toilet roll cylinders are also excellent for growing your seedlings in.

## GLASS JARS

• Jars with metal lids can be attached to the underside of shelves and used for the storage of nails, screws, nuts, bolts, etc., allowing them to be seen at a glance, and saving valuable shelf space.

• The same system can be used to store plant seeds — ideal for the serious gardeners who save their own seeds.

• Jars of various sizes are perfect for preserving homemade pickles and jams. Those jars that have the Agee type twist seal lids can be used for bottling fruit or high-acid tomatoes.

• Some jars are specially shaped to be used as drinking glasses when original contents are finished. Look out for these when you are shopping.

## KITCHEN SCRAPS

Composting your kitchen vegetables and fruit scraps will not only eliminate unnecessary garbage collection, but will also help to improve your garden soil.

For those of you who don't have a compost heap or bin, dig a hole in your garden, put your scraps in, sprinkle over a cup of dolomite, moisten slightly, and cover with soil. In a week or two the earthworms will have the soil workable. A great way to get rid of your food scraps, and improve your garden with high-quality soil.

This method also works successfully when establishing new garden areas — just mark each spot as you dispose of your scraps so that you don't dig there again. Once the designated area has been entirely composted, you can then establish your new garden.

*See also Compost.*

## NEWSPAPERS

• Windows and mirrors can be cleaned with wads of newspaper that have been wrung out in vinegar water — dissolve 2 teaspoons of vinegar in every 2 cups (500 ml) of water. Shine with sheets of clean newspaper.

Discarded paper can then be torn up and added to the compost heap. *See Compost.*

• They can be shredded and added to the compost or used as a ground level base layer when establishing new garden beds. *See Garden (No-dig Garden).*

• Slugs can be discouraged by placing newspaper barriers in their paths. *See Garden (Pest Control).*

• Newspaper logs make excellent fuel for slow combustion heaters or stoves. Roll the newspaper, tightly from the bottom of the page, around a broom handle until it is about 5 cm thick. Remove the handle, tie the log with string and then soak it in cooking oil. When dry, roll more newspaper around it until it is 10 cm thick and secure again with string.

Paper logs will burn for several hours.

• Balls of dampened newspaper are excellent for cleaning dust from dirty flyscreens.

## PAPER PRODUCTS

• Egg cartons can be used as seedling propagation trays. When ready to plant out, cut out the individual cups and remove the bottoms. The cardboard will eventually decompose into the soil.

• Labels from canned foods can be used as notepaper for shopping lists, phone messages, and so on, after which they can then be added to the compost heap.

## PLASTIC CONTAINERS

• Plastic bottles of all sizes make handy funnels — simple cut out the bottom with a sharp knife. If you need a fine filter, stretch a piece of clean nylon pantyhose over the neck of the bottle.

• Two litre bottles, or larger, can be used to greenhouse early seedlings. Cut the bottoms off, leave the caps on, and place over planted out seedlings at night until all danger of frost is gone.

• Roll-on deodorant bottles with removable balls make ideal painting pens for young children. Fill with non-toxic paint — less mess than paint brushes and small fingers.

• Large ice-cream containers make excellent planters for growing kitchen herbs. Pierce a few holes in the bottom, add a 15 mm layer of clean gravel and add soil mixture appropriate to the herb's needs.

## Rags and Old Clothes

• Old towelling can be turned into presoaped bathroom wash bags. Make a drawstring bag, hang in your shower recess and fill with leftover soap pieces.

• Old towels and nappies, when cut up, make ideal polishing cloths. Or sew the best pieces of them together to make beach or picnic rugs — dye them a favourite colour.

• Old hand-knitted jumpers that have lost their shape completely can be unravelled and reknitted. Unravel the wool into skeins, tie, and then wash it.

• A large jumper can find new life as a bolero for a small person. Remove the sleeves, cut it open down the front, and bind the edges with a brightly printed material.

• Any leftover bits of rag and clothing, providing that they are made out of natural fibres, can be cut up into small pieces and added to the compost heap.

## Tyres

Recycling old car tyres does present a problem, because there is not a great deal commercial recyclers can do with them. However, as a waste product, discarded tyres can be recovered for many uses around the home. They will cost you absolutely nothing — you will find that tyre dealers are more than happy to give them away.

One of the most effective ways that I have used them is for growing potatoes. Not only will you require very little space, but you will also be rewarded with a bumper crop. A great idea for small backyards, or wherever garden space is limited.

Place a seed potato in the centre of an old tyre and cover it with 15 cm of soil or compost. As the plant grows add soil (or compost or mulch) to just below the growing tip of the shoot, and keep adding more tyres as required. Usually 5 to 6 tyres will be sufficient.

Once the last tyre is full of dirt, allow to leaf up and flower. Your potato crop is ready for harvesting when the flowers die back and the stalks begin to wilt.

To harvest, simply brush the dirt away as you remove each tyre and then pick the potatoes.

Four to 6 stacks of tyres, planted out twice a year, will provide more than enough potatoes for the average family's needs.

## REFRIGERATOR

*See Kitchen.*

## RHEUMATISM

*See Aches and Pains, Pets (Rheumatism).*

## RHUBARB

*See Insecticides (Garden).*

## RODENTS (RATS AND MICE)

Both rats and mice are more than just a nuisance, they're a pest — apart from the damage they can cause, they spread disease.

The best way to control rodents is adequate prevention. Install vermin wire to deny access to under-house crawl spaces, wall cavities and roofs. Fit rubber extruders to external doors and connecting garage doors and ensure that insect screens fit tightly — mice and rats can squeeze through incredibly small spaces.

Clean up areas of brush and long grass around the house and along fences, and open up the areas around sheds and other outbuildings. This will make rodents visible and more susceptible to attack by their natural enemies.

If you feel squeamish about using traps you can try the following repellents.

• Blocks of camphor scattered around the place in ceilings keep mice and rats away. So does fresh mint placed near mouse holes or a mixture of mint leaves, cayenne pepper and cottonwool soaked in peppermint oil.

• Mint and tansy in cupboards will repel mice.

• Rags saturated with turpentine and placed in ceilings and other haunts will repel them.

However, once rodents have gained access to your home, no deterrent will keep them from a favourite meal. Baits provide a safe alternative to chemical poisons, and also send the rodents away to die.

### Rodent Bait

*½ cup (60 g) cornflour*
*½ cup (130 g) cement*

Combine the ingredients, mixing thoroughly, and place small amounts in margarine tubs near entrance holes or runaways. For outside, place an ice-cream container that has had holes cut in its sides, over the margarine containers to provide protection from wet weather. Hold in place with a half brick.

Rodents will eat the mixture and go away to find water. The water reacts with the cement and kills them.

If you don't like the idea of using cement, replace it with plaster of Paris and mix to a dough with milk.

## TRAPS

Place traps along runways and other haunts. For large numbers of rodents locate a number of traps at right angles to each other, and instead of baiting them individually just scatter wheatgerm or cornmeal over them.

After the second kill rub traps with aniseed oil to disguise the odour. Before placing your traps, find the mouse hole and sprinkle baking powder or talcum powder in front of suspected openings. Their tell-tale tracks will be seen next day if they have been there.

## ROOM FRESHENERS

*See Air Fresheners, Incense.*

## ROSEMARY (*ROSEMARINUS OFFICINALIS*)

Rosemary, a much-loved herb, is decorative, aromatic and has a multitude of uses. It definitely deserves to have a place in any kind of garden and brings a smile to the lips of all who breathe in its country-garden freshness.

Cosmetically, it is cleansing, stimulating and restorative, and can either be used as an infusion or as an essential oil. It is beneficial for the hair, as well as being a deodorant, a mouthwash and a bath herb. When included in bath water it will stimulate the circulation, soften the skin, relieve stiff joints and relax aching muscles.

Blended with peppermint leaves and taken as tea it is an excellent tonic for mild digestive upsets, and will aid digestion and appetite.

## Rosemary Wine

This herbal wine is a good general tonic and an aid to relaxation.

*2 cups (500 ml) white wine*
*4 sprigs fresh rosemary*

Bruise the rosemary sprigs and put them in a ceramic pot. Add the wine, cover, and leave to infuse for 2 days. Strain and drink a small wineglassful when needed.

## Rosemary Hair Rinse

*6 fresh rosemary sprigs*
*5 cups (1¼ litres) distilled water*

Put the rosemary sprigs in an enamel or stainless steel pan, add distilled water, bring to the boil and simmer for 30 minutes. Keep the pan covered to prevent the vapour from escaping. Remove from heat, allow to cool, and use as a final rinse after washing your hair, massaging well into the scalp.

*See also Teas (Herbal).*

*Did you know ...*

that rosemary is a symbol of remembrance, fidelity and friendship? In times gone by it was believed to strengthen the memory too.

## ROSEWATER

Use 900 g of fresh rose petals or 600 g of dried petals. Put the flowers in a ceramic casserole dish, covered with distilled water, and place in an oven that has been preheated to 220°C. When the water reaches boiling point replace the casserole lid and leave in the oven for a further 15 minutes. Remove, allow to cool while covered, then strain through muslin.

Use in cooking or as a bath additive.

## RUST

### CLOTHING
Rust stains can be removed from clothing by soaking the clothing in a strong solution of lemon juice and salt. Leave in the sun to dry, then wash.

### GARDEN TOOLS
A good way to keep your garden tools both clean and rust-free is to build a cleaning pit. All you need is a hole near the entrance to your toolshed, lined with old bricks. Fill it with sand and next time you change the oil in your car, just pour the old oil into the sand and mix it up. Try to maintain a sandy texture without too much oil.

Before putting garden tools away, work them in the mix for a few seconds, and they should be clean, oiled and ready for storage.

## SALT

*See Dietary Substitutes.*

## SAUCEPANS

• For dirty saucepans that don't respond to steel wool, add cold water and 2 teaspoons of bicarbonate of soda to the pot and bring to the boil. When cool, clean off with steel wool.

• To clean off burnt food from a saucepan, cover the base with water and add a small chopped onion. Bring to the boil and boil for about 10 minutes. The food will then clean off.

• Stainless steel saucepans can be cleaned with soapy water or a cloth dampened with vinegar.

• Enamel pots and pans, if brown, can be cleaned by scouring with coarse salt, then washing in hot soda water.

• Stubborn stains can be removed from aluminium pots by simmering in a strong solution of white vinegar for 20 minutes. Wash and use a wooden spoon to scrape.

### POT SCOURER

Before there were steel wool and synthetic scourers, horsetail stems (*Equisetum arvense*) were used. They have a fine sandpaper surface of silica crystals which will easily clear even the dirtiest pots and pans.

To clean pots, rub a handful of the leafless stems on their surface, then rinse away any residual green stains.

This herb readily grows in the home garden, except places where the soil is extremely alkaline. You can get it from nurseries that specialise in herbs and also from general nurseries.

*See also Bicarbonate of Soda, Cleaning (Horsetail Metal Cleaner), Copper, Dishwashing.*

## SEDATIVE

*See Chamomile, First Aid, Stress, Teas (Herbal).*

## SHAMPOO

*See Hair Care.*

## SHOES

### Waterproof Polish

The following recipe is for a neutral-coloured cream that will keep leather shoes both supple and waterproof.

*50 g grated white soap*
*4 cups (1 litre) natural turpentine*
*4 cups (1 litre) boiling water*
*150 g beeswax*
*50 g Vaseline*

Place the soap shavings in a ceramic bowl, add the turpentine and stand for 24 hours. Blend with boiling water, stirring continually to dissolve any remaining soap.

Melt the beeswax and Vaseline together in a double pan over a medium heat until completely liquid. Remove from heat, add the soap/turpentine mixture and stir constantly until cold. Store in a wide-mouthed glass jar.

Coloured polish can be made by adding different earth oxide pigments (available from hardware or builder's supply stores).

To colour the polish, mix the powdered oxide with the water-turpentine-soap mixture until you get the colour you want.

### SHOE ODOUR

Eliminate shoe odour by sprinkling powdered herbs in shoes each evening. Use dried chamomile, hyssop or pennyroyal, and reduce to a powder by rubbing through a fine wire sieve.

Alternatively, mix sufficient aromatic oil, a drop at a time, with bicarbonate of soda, and sprinkle this in your shoes.

*See also Leather, Lemon.*

## SHOWER (AROMATIC)

*See Stress.*

## SILVERFISH

Silverfish in the house are a nuisance and can cause irreparable damage to books and other valuable documents. Often the first sign of this pest is chewed pages of a precious or favourite volume. By then it is too late and the damage is done. Prevention is the best protection and should become a regular housekeeping activity.

• Regular vacuuming of both books and bookshelves is essential, not forgetting books stored in boxes or cupboards. Remove books from shelves and storage at least once a year and thoroughly vacuum, including crevices and cracks in shelves, cupboards and storage boxes.
• Vacuum books that are to be stored away for a long time, then place in plastic bags with sprigs of lavender or cottonwool soaked in lavender oil, seal, and leave in the sun for about 6 hours.
• Treat baseboards, table legs and cracks in cupboards and shelves with a mixture of borax and sugar. Place traps, consisting of 1 part molasses to 2 parts vinegar, in corners.
• Wipe vacuumed shelves liberally with lavender oil — this will deter silverfish for up to a year if the oil is potent.
• Place bunches of dried lavender in storage boxes and cupboards, or a mixture of lavender and bay leaves.
• Cinnamon bark pieces, dried wormwood leaves and the dried leaves of tansy and mint crumbled together and put into muslin bags will help to keep silverfish from your drawers and cupboards .

## SILVERWARE

Tarnish can be removed from silverware by boiling up several handfuls of parsley and dipping silver into it. Or you can apply a little whiting (from the chemist) dissolved in methylated spirits.

To clean add 1½ teaspoons of salt and 1½ tablespoons of bicarbonate of soda to 4 cups (1 litre) of water. Bring to the boil and drop silver cutlery in. Boil it for 3 minutes, then polish it with a soft cloth. For badly tarnished sliver add a piece of heavy duty aluminium foil — this will react with the bicarbonate of soda to lift the tarnish.

*See also Cleaning (Horsetail Metal Cleaner).*

## SINUSITIS

With the arrival of spring, many suffer sinusitis and hayfever. There are safe, natural treatments which won't make you drowsy and have no unwanted side effects.

The traditional approach to sinus and hayfever relief uses a combination of vitamins, minerals and herbs. In particular vitamins C and A, and zinc and the herbs horseradish and fenugreek: vitamin C to reduce mucus, vitamin A and the mineral zinc to reduce the susceptibility to infections and to increase the health of the epithelial tissue lining and sinuses, helping them against further attack by invading allergy proteins. Iron phosphate and potassium chloride are also important to reduce inflammation and mucus discharge.

Include foods such as natural unprocessed bran, soya beans, oatmeal, raisins, sultanas, celery, cucumber, lettuce, cabbage, tomato, yellow vegetables, sprouted grains, green and red peppers, parsley, and any fresh fruit in your diet.

The herbs horseradish and fenugreek are available in a supplement from your local health food store. Horseradish helps to remove mucus from the nasal and sinus passages. It contains a compound called Sinigrin which acts as a decongestant.

Fenugreek helps soothe irritated nasal and sinus tissues, and also helps to dry up catarrh (mucus in the throat and nose) that allergy sufferers are often prone to.

### Herbal Tea Remedy
Equal parts of thyme and fenugreek taken as tea will give relief.

*1 teaspoon dried herb*
*1¼ cups (300 ml) boiling water*

Infuse herb in boiling water. Cover, infuse for 3 minutes and strain into a cup. Take 1 cup 3 times daily.

## Herbal Inhalant

For sinusitis, a herbal inhalation will relieve nasal congestion.

*1 cup (50 g) peppermint leaves*
*½ cup (15 g) sage leaves*
*¼ cup (12.5 g) thyme leaves*
*4 cups (1 litre) boiling water*

Put all the herbs in a ceramic or glass bowl, add water, sit with your face over the bowl and drape a towel over your head to form a tent. Inhale the vapour for 5 to 10 minutes.

Alternatively, add 2 drops each of basil, eucalyptus, lavender and peppermint oils to a bowl containing 2½ cups (600 ml) boiling water and inhale as before.

Either inhalation procedure should not be repeated more than 3 times daily.

Inhalation can also be accomplished by putting 5 to 8 drops of oil on a handkerchief or tissue and taking 4 deep breaths — an ideal portable treatment when in bed, at work or while travelling.

When the handkerchief is not in use, you should place it against your breastbone, where it will continue to work.

## ALLERGY SUFFERERS

Cod-liver oil is an old standby and natural food supplement. Taken as prescribed it will help allergy sufferers.

However, always consult a professional practitioner.

## SKIN CARE

Have you ever wondered just how and why it is we have lost the art and knowledge of using and making our own cosmetic preparations? Our great-grandmothers certainly knew the secrets of making lotions and creams from the herbs, flowers and fruit that they collected.

We have now gone full circle and are once again turning to Nature for the answers. We have begun to realise that Nature is the best, the purest, the most beneficial.

The following recipes will give you quick and easy-to-prepare treatments for natural skin care. All the ingredients can be found in your kitchen cupboard, health food store, chemist or local supermarket.

## CLEANSING
### Rose Cleansing Oil

*1 cup (250 ml) olive oil*
*1 tablespoon avocado oil*
*½ cup (125 ml) apricot kernel oil*
*½ cup (125 ml) jojoba oil*
*¼ teaspoon essential oil of rose*

Pour all the oils into a screwtop jar and shake vigorously.

To use, pour sufficient oil into a piece of cottonwool and gently apply to your face and neck until clean, using an outward and upward movement. Remove oily residue with an alcohol-free toning lotion or witch-hazel.

Store in the refrigerator if you are not using it daily.

### Toning Lotion

*25 drops of either rosemary, thyme or lavender essential oil*
*1 tablespoon cider vinegar*
*⅔ cup (150 ml) distilled water*

Dissolve the essential oil in the cider vinegar and then add this mixture to the distilled water. Store in a glass bottle with a tight-fitting lid.

Pour a little toner onto slightly damp cottonwool, and use the same upward and outward movement as you did with the cleanser. Avoid the delicate eye area.

## MOISTURISING
### Avocado Neck and Face Moisturiser

Avocado oil is an excellent moisturiser to use under make-up, particularly in drying winds. Fresh avocado on the face and neck is especially nourishing for the skin.

Scoop out the flesh from half an avocado and mash it up into pulp. Spread the pulp on the face and neck and lie down and relax for about 20 minutes while the oil of the fruit nourishes and moisturises your skin.

Remove with tissues, then dampened cottonwool.

## Avocado Oil Treatment

Take a large avocado and squeeze out the oil by crushing it in a bowl or in a blender and pressing the pulp through a fine sieve or through muslin. Put a few drops of oil in your bath, the rest on your face and soak for 10 minutes.

## Orange Oil

When eating oranges don't discard the peel, as it contains a lot of precious oil, good for face and body. Scratch the outer peel with a sharp pointed object, then squeeze the peel and you'll see the oil coming out. Gently rub the scoured peel directly onto your face or body.

## Strawberry Mask

You can make another simple moisturising treatment, with fresh strawberries, that you can use after cleansing and toning your skin.

Cut up and mash into a pulp sufficient fresh strawberries to spread all over the face and neck, leaving the eye area clear. Lie down for 20 minutes.

For an extra benefit, soak balls of cottonwool in a cold tea made from crushed fennel seeds and put them on your closed eyelids.

Rinse the mask off with warm water, then splash cold water all over the face and neck.

## HONEY

Honey was known to the ancient Greeks as the food of the gods because of its unique healing properties. It has always been used for rejuvenating purposes. It contains many vitamins and minerals — an excellent source of many of the B group vitamins, vitamin C, carotene and organic acids. It works well as a natural skin softener, an antiseptic, and is also an ideal ingredient for natural skin care preparations. Honey cleanses and heals, easily removing dead skin cells, and moisturises; it is very effective with dry, chapped skin and windblown or damaged lips.

When using honey for the skin you should always use natural unprocessed honey and not brands which have been boiled during processing. Good health food shops should carry some brands that have not been excessively boiled.

Here are a few suggestions for a honey-nurtured complexion.

## Face Cleanser

Mix together equal amounts of clear honey and wheatgerm oil and spread it over your face, avoiding the eyes. Keep on for 15 minutes, relaxing while you wait. Wash off with lukewarm water and then splash cold water on the face to close the pores. Pat dry with a soft towel.

Honey and wheatgerm together will make an excellent facial cleanser which is especially effective in removing blackheads.

*See also Make-up Remover.*

## Face Mask

*1 tablespoon clear honey*
*1 teaspoon glycerine*
*1 egg white*
*fine-ground oatmeal*

Mix the first three ingredients together with sufficient oatmeal to make a paste. Apply to face and leave on for 30 minutes, then wash off with tepid water.

*See also Chamomile (Oatmeal Scrub), Fennel, Jojoba.*

## Orange-honey Facial Mask

A refreshing and revitalising treatment for all skin types, being gentle enough to apply to sensitive areas.

*3 tablespoons honey*
*juice of ½ orange*

Warm the honey until it is fluid, add the orange juice, and apply to facial skin until thick enough.

Leave on for at least 15 minutes, then massage the face with an upward rotary movement. Rinse with tepid water and allow the face to dry of its own accord.

## Rejuvenating Mask

*3 tablespoons honey*
*3 tablespoons olive oil*
*gauze*

Heat the honey and olive oil in an enamel pan, stirring constantly until the mixture forms a smooth, viscous paste.

Cut the gauze into 10 cm strips, dip them in the mixture, then apply them to the face at the hottest tolerable temperature until all skin is covered. Cold compresses can be applied to the eyelids to protect the eyes.

Leave the mask on for 20 minutes, at least, then rinse it off carefully with lukewarm water, followed by a little diluted cider vinegar (1 tablespoon vinegar to ⅔ cup (150 ml) distilled water) to leave the skin feeling fresh.

Alternatively, replace the diluted cider vinegar with distilled water to which has been added a few drops of essential rose oil (3 to 4 drops oil to 4 cups (1 litre) of water).

### SKIN PROTECTION

Winter winds are drying and damaging to facial skin and hands, causing it to become scaly, or in severe cases chapped and split.

Natural protection with a herbal oil moisturiser will keep skin soft and supple always.

### Moisturising Oil

*2 tablespoons ground almonds*
*3 drops rose oil*

2 cups (500 ml) distilled water
½ teaspoon sugar
6 drops friars balsam, from the chemist

Mix the ground almonds and rose oil with the distilled water and allow to steep for 60 minutes. Strain through fine muslin, add the sugar and tincture of benzoin. Bottle and seal until needed.

*See also Aftershave, Aloe Vera, Chamomile, Cream, Elder Tree, Essential Oils, Feet, Fennel, Hands, Jojoba, Lips, Sun Exposure, Violets, Yarrow.*

## SOAP

Recycling cooking oil or fat and turning it into soap is very easy to do. Making your own biodegradable soap will not only help our environment, but will save money as well, and is good, clean fun.

Save used cooking oil and fat in glass jars, empty milk cartons or other containers (not aluminium or metal) until you have enough.

The first step is to remove any salt from the fat. To do this, place meat or bacon fat in a saucepan and cover with water, bring to boil, remove from heat, and allow to cool. When cool, the fat can be skimmed off and meat or crackling scraped from the bottom. Put in a clean pan and clarify and strain.

Clarify fat using just enough heat to melt it. Skim off any remaining pieces of meat and then strain through muslin cloth or one of those old-fashioned fat strainers. (They can still be purchased from some supermarkets or hardware stores.)

You may also need to soften your tap water, since hard water makes lousy soap. To soften it, simply add washing soda.

*See also Cleaning, Dog Washing Soap.*

### Basic Hard Soap

500 g caustic soda (see warning below)
8 cups (2 litres) soft water
3 kg salt-free, clarified fat

Put the water in a large ceramic bowl or enamel pot and add the caustic soda, stirring until it is completely dissolved. The mixture becomes extremely hot and must be set aside until lukewarm.

At the same time melt the fat and allow it to cool but not solidify again. Add the caustic solution to the fat and stir for 5 minutes. Pour into moulds and keep in a warm spot for 24 hours, cut into bars, and then cure for several weeks before using. This will ensure that any free caustic is incorporated.

Empty milk cartons that have been thoroughly rinsed make ideal soap-making moulds. Simply peel away the carton once the soap has solidified and cut into bars.

If you wish to have an aromatic soap, add a few drops of your favourite flower or herb essential oil just before pouring the mixture into the moulds. Make sure that the oil is well mixed.

## Soft Soap
A soft soap can be made by replacing cooking fat with new or used vegetable oil.

*500 g caustic soda*
*6 cups (1½ litres) soft water*
*6 cups (1½ litres) vegetable oil*

Prepare the same way as for Basic Hard Soap, adding caustic solution to unheated oil.

WARNING:
Caustic soda is very corrosive. It will burn skin, aluminium, tin and clothing. Avoid fumes, spillage and splashing and wear rubber gloves when adding caustic soda to water.

It can make you choke if fumes are inhaled. Use a large, wide bowl when making the caustic solution.

Keep caustic solution out of the reach of children as it BOILS.

## FIRST AID
Have a bowl of neutraliser handy while soapmaking — any type of common vinegar will work well.

Wash the affected part immediately and thoroughly in water. Remove and soak any affected clothing. Work in an airy place and seek fresh air if fumes are inhaled.

If a burn to the skin should occur, first wash the affected area, then cover it with a wet, cold cloth. You should seek medical help immediately.

Keep your face well away from the pouring caustic solution (lye), as an alkaline burn to the eyes means permanent loss of sight. Wear protective glasses. Should any lye come in contact with the eyes rinse immediately with clean water and seek medical help promptly.

## SOAP SCRAPS

Don't throw out those small leftover pieces of soap! Instead, recycle them into useable new bars or other soap products.

• For soap bars, place scraps in a saucepan, cover with water and allow to soak for 24 hours, giving an occasional stir. Bring to the boil, remove from heat and add a tablespoon of vegetable oil to each cupful. Pour into moulds and allow to harden for 2 weeks before use.

If you want to use it after 24 hours, omit the vegetable oil from the soap mixture.

• To make liquid soap, place leftover pieces of soap in a jar of hot water, then add some lemon juice and glycerine and shake well.

• Soap scraps can also be used for a pre-soaped bathroom wash bag. Make a drawstring bag from old towelling, fill with leftovers, and hang in your shower recess. It will save on soap and is easy for small children to handle.

## SPIDER BITE

Harmful species, such as funnel-web and red-back, should be treated professionally and immediate help should be sought.

Harmless spiders only leave an itchy swelling. This can be treated by applying a concoction of 3 drops lavender oil and 2 drops chamomile oil diluted in 5 ml of vodka. Dab on the affected area 3 times during 1 day should be sufficient.

*See also Insect Bites and Stings.*

## STAINS

*See Bicarbonate of Soda, Blood Stains, Carpet, Curtains, Ink Stains, Laundry, Lemon, Lipstick, Rust, Upholstery, Urine, Wallpaper, Wax.*

## STAINLESS STEEL

Clean with soapy water or a cloth dampened with white vinegar.

## STOVE

*See Oven.*

## STRAWBERRIES

**Did you know ...**

that strawberries make an excellent astringent for facial skin? Crush ½ cup (80 g) of strawberries and apply to your face with cottonwool. Leave to dry for a few minutes and then rinse off.

Also, blend ½ cup (80 g) of crushed strawberries thoroughly with almond oil to make a soothing and smoothing night moisturising cream. Apply to your face just before going to bed.

*See Skin Care.*

## STRESS

Luxuriating in an aromatic bath is a great way to revive or relax your body. Essential oils added to your bath water release their special properties to penetrate your skin, as well as exerting their therapeutic value through the inhaled vapour. For maximum effect close all windows and the bathroom door.

### BATH

At night run a bath using chamomile, jasmine or lavender. Add about 4 drops of oil once the hot water has settled.

Lie in the bath for 10 minutes with your eyes closed, and take deep relaxing breaths. The relaxing vapours will envelop you.

### AROMATIC SHOWER

In the morning you can enjoy the benefits of fragrant oils with an aromatic shower. Oils that will invigorate are thyme, bergamot, marjoram and rosemary.

To start, dilute 10 drops of your favourite oil with 15 ml of odourless vegetable oil. Rub your entire body with a little of this fragrant oil, diluted half-and-half with water. Plug the shower drain and while showering sprinkle in the same aromatics as the water collects. Your feet will benefit from the fragrant soak, while the ascending aroma will relax your mind.

*See also Juniper.*

## STUDENTS

For students who feel the stress of approaching exams, essential oils will help you cope and remain alert during long hours of study. Try any of the following:

**Basil** — to clear the head.

**Bergamot** — to bring freshness.

**Cardamom** — for reducing mental fatigue.

**Lavender** — ideal for physical and mental tension.

**Rose** — to lift your spirits.

**Tangerine** — energising.

Simply add a drop of oil to one page in every book you are using.

*See also Bath (Aromatic), Chamomile, Insomnia,*
*Relaxation, Teas (Herbal).*

## SUGAR SUBSTITUTES

*See Dietary Substitutes.*

## SUN EXPOSURE

The beach and sunbaking are almost synonymous with summer fun, but likewise this fun can quite easily turn into disaster. Though a tan is still often perceived as beautiful and healthy, excessive, prolonged exposure to the sun is a major cause of skin cancers.

Skin damage may occur after 12 to 20 minutes exposure to sunlight. And this 12 to 20 minutes can add up by just hanging out the washing or walking to the shops. So all day at the beach, sport, gardening and other leisure activities obviously means greater exposure to the sun's harmful rays.

To avoid skin damage, and the possibility of skin cancer, it is essential to wear a sunscreen, and keep covered up as much as possible, when exposed to the sun. It is also preferable to stay out of the sun between 11 am and 2 pm during summer.

## Herbal Sunscreen Cream

This is the cream my family uses when spending time out in the sun and it has proved successful in blocking about half of the sun's burning rays. However, you must also take a sensible approach towards dress, including the wearing of a wide-brimmed hat, when using this cream, to get the most benefit.

*¾ cup (180 ml) very strong tea*
*¼ cup (50 ml) anhydrous lanolin*
*¼ cup (60 ml) cold pressed sesame oil*
*20 ml carrot oil*
*¼ cup (70 g) calamine powder*
   *8 drops essential oil of rosemary*

In a ceramic teapot brew very strong tea, using 3 teabags and infusing for 30 minutes.

Put the lanolin, sesame oil, carrot oil, calamine powder and 3 tablespoons of tea in an electric blender and whirl at low speed. When they are completely blended increase the speed and pour in the remaining tea in a thin, steady stream. Add the rosemary oil last. Store the mixture in a suitable jar with a tight-fitting lid.

### AFTER-SUN SOOTHER

We are all aware of the dangers of spending too much time in the sun, especially if exposed skin is left unprotected. Even when you are taking precautions, a day outdoors in summer can still leave your skin feeling hot and sticky. To remedy this you need to apply a natural, after-sun soother to cool and refresh the skin.

• Cut a large cucumber into chunks and process in a food blender. Wash the skin then gently apply the cucumber.

• Cold chamomile tea or elderflower tea is also an effective remedy for soothing and cooling the skin.

• Elderflowers can be made into a soothing ointment to relieve facial soreness due to exposure to sea air. *See Elder Tree.*

## All Day Soother

Keep the following skin soother in your bag whenever you're out-of-doors.

*4 tablespoons each of*
*watermelon juice*
*cucumber juice*
*aloe vera juice*
*rosewater*
*witch-hazel (from the chemist)*
*cold chamomile tea*
*vodka*

First you need to prepare the cucumber and watermelon juice; cut the fruit into large chunks after their skin has been thoroughly washed. Process the fruit in a juice extractor, then boil the juice for 5 minutes, skimming off any scum. Remove from heat, cool and allow to drip through filter paper and add required amount to recipe.

Mix the juices, rosewater, witch-hazel solution and cold chamomile tea and add two parts liquid preparation to one part vodka. Leave this to stand for 12 hours and then drip it through filter paper, continuing to do so until it is clear. Store in a tightly sealed bottle.

Apply generously to skin, rubbing in well.

## Sunburn Lotion

This lotion will ease mild sunburn and prevent further moisture loss from the skin.

*50 g glycerine*
*40 ml aloe vera juice*
*10 ml wheatgerm oil*
*10 ml jojoba oil*

Mix all the ingredients, then beat them vigorously until they are completely emulsified. Store the lotion in a tightly sealed bottle. Use generously on affected skin.

*See also Skin Care, Vinegar (Herbal).*

## TANNIN STAINS

*See Bicarbonate of Soda, Laundry.*

## TAPS

Chrome taps and other fittings can be cleaned and stains can be removed with a cloth dipped in bicarbonate of soda. Polish the taps with a soft, clean cloth.

## TEAS, HERBAL

Since ancient times, herbal teas have been used to ease certain ailments. Today they are just as appropriate, and also provide a refreshing taste alternative to conventional teas.

Herbal teas are readily available from both health food stores and supermarkets, and are sold singularly or in blends. So next time you feel like a cuppa, try a herbal tea instead!

Use only a ceramic teapot for making herbal tea. Aluminium, or other metals, can quite easily mar the brew.

### TYPES OF TEA

Alfalfa has a bland taste, but is quite acceptable when blended with mint, lemon verbena and/or honey. It is a rich source of iron, phosphorus, potassium and magnesium. It is thought to relieve arthritis and other twinges and pains, to build the body, and improve digestion.

Chamomile has a light, apple-like taste and is rich in calcium. It is used to soothe gastro-intestinal disorders, relieve menstrual pain, reduce fever and restlessness in children, and is said to induce sound sleep and calm an overactive brain. It will also help teething children, expel worms, and help in the treatment of children with red, inflamed eyes when used as an eye bath or compress.

Make a tea by pouring 5 tablespoons of boiling water over 10 g of dried chamomile flowers, infuse for an hour and strain. Heat gently to drink hot, and sweeten with honey or serve as iced tea. Or follow the directions for prepacked tea bags.

*See also Chamomile.*

Lemongrass is very palatable and an excellent first tea to try. This herb is rich in vitamin A and is considered excellent for purifying the skin and refining its texture.

Nettle has a very bland taste, but is palatable with a little mint or honey. The tea contains vitamin D, iron, calcium and other trace elements. It is traditionally used as a blood tonic and thought to stimulate digestion and increase lactation in nursing mothers. Its astringent qualities will relieve urinary disorders, rheumatic problems and colds, it is said.

Many people find the taste of peppermint soothing, refreshing, and delicately fruity. It is reputed to disperse congestion, and relieve indigestion, nausea, headaches, abdominal pain, cramp and vomiting.

Raspberry leaf has a fruity, soothing taste, and is traditionally recommended to expectant mothers for relief of morning sickness, to ease childbirth and assist lactation. It is also said to tone up mucous membranes. However, if taken in excess, it can cause uterine contractions, so caution is required. It is not recommended for use in the last three months of pregnancy.

Rosemary has a fragrant, aromatic taste. It has long been revered as an all-purpose tonic that freshens breath, induces sleep, alleviates headache and strengthens the nerves. The cooled tea can be rubbed into the scalp as a hair tonic.

Sage leaf has a stimulating, slightly bitter taste. It has a long history of use for rheumatic complaints, calming the nerves, soothing a sore throat (gargle) and as a tonic for the liver and brain.

*See also Feverfew.*

## TEAS FOR SPECIFIC COMPLAINTS

The following lists the various teas that can be used for specific complaints either on their own or as a mixture.

• Tonic — borage, sage, mint, rosemary, dandelion, blackberry, raspberry and strawberry leaf.

- Infections, coughs and colds — angelica, elderflower, yarrow, peppermint, thyme, rose hip, aniseed, horehound, fenugreek and lemongrass.
- Cold and 'Flu Blend — equal parts elderflower, peppermint and yarrow. One cup every 2 hours to help relieve symptoms.
- Cooling the body and reducing fever — lemon balm, borage, peppermint, elderflower and yarrow.
- For the liver — angelica, parsley and fenugreek.
- For the kidneys and diuretic — celery seed, dandelion and parsley.
- Indigestion, stomach ache and flatulence — dill, peppermint, caraway, fennel, aniseed, lovage, rosemary, chamomile, coriander, sage, thyme, spearmint and lemon balm.
- Nausea — dandelion, spearmint, peppermint and basil.
- Rheumatic pain — parsley, angelica and celery.
- Mild sedative, relaxation — linden (lime) flower, chamomile, lemon verbena, and orange flower.

*See also Fingernails (Tea), Sinusitis.*

## Substitute for Conventional Tea

Natural herbal blends contain no caffeine or tannin, both very strong stimulants. The following recipe is an ideal introduction to herbal teas, especially for those people who are used to drinking ordinary tea.

*dried red clover flower*
*dried dandelion leaf*
*dried peppermint leaf*

Blend equal parts of these herbs and store in an airtight glass jar.

To make the tea, put 1 level teaspoon of dried herb for each individual into a ceramic teapot, plus 1 for the pot, and pour in boiling water. Infuse for 5 minutes, then strain into cups.

## Oatstraw and Cinnamon Tea

*2 teaspoons oatstraw*
*1 slice fresh ginger root*
*5 cm cinnamon stick*

Brew all together and leave for 5 minutes before serving. Strain into individual cups.

## MAKING HERBAL TEAS

Unless otherwise directed for prepackaged herbal teas, follow the directions for the conventional tea substitute.

For individual cups, pour in hot water, cover, infuse for 3 minutes, and strain into another cup.

Unless otherwise directed, the following proportions apply for brewing herbal teas.

1 tablespoon fresh herb or 1 level teaspoon dried herb to 1¼ cups (300 ml) of boiling water.

A tea can be drunk at any time during the day, and you can add honey, a slice of lemon, or a tablespoon of orange flower water or rosewater.

When making a flower tea the procedure should be modified as follows:

First bring the measured amount of water to boil in an enamel or stainless steel pan. Add the flowers, replace the lid, and simmer for 1 minute. Remove from heat and allow to infuse for 3 minutes, then strain into individual cups.

In summer, teas can be chilled in the refrigerator and drunk with the addition of iced mineral water or fresh fruit juice.

## TEA STAINS

*See Bicarbonate of Soda, Laundry.*

## TEA TREE OIL

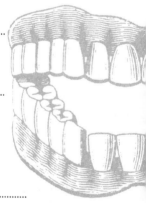

*Did you know ...*
that tea tree oil is a strong, natural antiseptic oil, good for insect bites and fungal problems?

## TEETH

Healthy teeth and a sparkling smile are not produced only by proprietary brand toothpastes, which quite often promise all sorts of amazing things. Your teeth and gums can be kept in tip-top condition by just cleaning them with herbs and other natural, safe ingredients.

## Simple Tooth Powder

A quick and simple tooth powder can be made by combining sea salt and bicarbonate of soda.

*2 tablespoons fine sea salt*
*3 tablespoons bicarbonate of soda*

Mix ingredients together thoroughly and store in a dry, airtight glass jar or other suitable container. To use, shake a little of the mixture into your hand and pick it up with a damp toothbrush.

## Herbal Toothpowder

*15 g fresh sage leaves*
*10 g fresh peppermint leaves*
*25 g coarse sea salt*

Mix the herbs and salt together and then spread them out on a baking tray. Place in a preheated oven (150°C) for 20 minutes, or until the herbs are crisp and dry. Reduce to a powder by rubbing through a fine wire sieve and store in a dry, airtight jar.

To use, shake a little of the mixture into your hand and pick it up with a damp toothbrush.

Sweet breath and a fresh tasting mouth are an important part of maintaining a holistic approach to natural health. Your personality radiates with the added confidence of good oral hygiene. Try this mouthwash.

## Herbal Mouthwash

*2 teaspoons dried sage*
*1 teaspoon dried rosemary*
*1 teaspoon dried peppermint*
*2 cups (500 ml) boiling water*
*½ cup (125 ml) brandy or cider vinegar*

Place all the herbs in a ceramic bowl and pour the boiling water over them. Add the brandy, or cider vinegar, cover and steep for 2 hours. Strain through fine muslin and then drip through filter paper. Store in a tightly sealed bottle.

Use as a soothing gargle or refreshing mouthwash as needed.

*See also Aloe Vera, First Aid (Toothache).*

## THROAT LOZENGE

To sooth a persistent cough, take a horehound cough lozenge.

Boil equal parts of fresh horehound juice and sugar until it sets, then cut into squares. Store in an airtight jar and keep moisture-free.

*See also Colds and Flu.*

## TICKS

Spring and summer can be a particularly bad time for ticks on the family dog or cat, especially if you live in a tick-infested area. Search your pet's fur daily, paying particular attention to the head, neck, ears, nostrils, lips and between the toes. Remove the tick by grasping between your thumb and forefinger and tugging sharply. And remember, both the head and body of the tick must come out — use a needle if necessary. If you feel that the thumb technique of tick removal is too difficult you can use a pair of tweezers. Make sure you grip the head firmly and not just the body.

Give an infusion of bracken shoots as an antidote to tick poisoning — it can save an animal's life if the ticks are found in time. If paralysis symptoms occur, immediately seek veterinary attention. Apply a tick repellent if you live in a tick-infested area.

### HERBAL ANTIDOTE

Bracken tea, made from an infusion of the shoots, will save a dog or cat's life if given in time. The tea is an antidote to tick poisoning.

To prepare, place a handful of bracken shoots in a ceramic bowl and pour boiling water over them. Infuse until the liquid is cool, strain and administer a cupful.

Remember though, your pet won't jump with joy and readily gulp tea down. As with most pet remedies you'll need to take a firm grip and pour it down the animal's throat.

### Tick Repellent

Apply a tick repellent weekly to your pet if you live in an area where ticks are bad, reapplying after rain or bathing.

*60 g powdered derris*
*2½ tablespoons eucalyptus oil*
*2½ tablespoons methylated spirits*
*16 cups (4 litres) water*

Dissolve the derris in the water and the oil in the methylated spirits, then mix the two thoroughly.

Wash the pet with warm soapy water, then rub the repellent lotion thoroughly through the animal's fur.

Alternatively, dust your animal's fur with powdered derris, again working it well in with your fingers. This may need to be applied more than once a week. Derris is a safe, organic substance which breaks down in sunlight in a few days. (However, it is deadly to fish, so keep your dog away from fish ponds or creeks.)

## TILES

Bicarbonate of soda will remove mould and mildew from small areas.

*See also Bathroom, Floors (Cleaning).*

## TIMBER STAIN

All wood surfaces can be sealed and preserved with a natural timber stain made from warm linseed oil. Thin the first coat with 20 per cent natural turpentine and the second coat with 10 per cent. The last coat should be straight linseed oil. Allow 2 weeks between each coat.

## TRAVEL SICKNESS

*See First Aid, Pets (Travel Sickness).*

## TOOTHACHE

*See First Aid.*

## TYRES

*See Recycling.*

## ULCERS

*See Aloe Vera.*

## UPHOLSTERY

### LEATHER

Stains on leather furniture can be removed by rubbing with eucalyptus oil, using a circular motion. Test a small section first in a spot that is not noticeable.

### FABRIC

For day-to-day cleaning use a diluted soapwort solution
*See Urine (Dog and Cat).*

For extra stubborn stains spot-clean with the same solution, undiluted, or the following dry-cleaning paste. Use on natural fibres only. Mix sufficient fuller's earth with water to form a paste and cover the soiled area. Allow to dry, then brush or vacuum off.

## URINE

### DOG AND CAT

To remove stains, sponge the area with a diluted mixture of warm soapwort solution. Place 4 tablespoons of dried soapwort in an enamel or stainless steel pan and add enough distilled water to cover. Boil for 10 minutes, cool, and strain through muslin cloth. Dilute 2 to 1 by volume.

### ODOUR

Add 6 to 12 drops of lavender oil to a cup of bicarbonate of soda, mixing in well with your hands. Sprinkle over the affected spot with a flour sifter, leave for 2 hours and vacuum up.

# VACUUM FLASK COOKING

*See Cooking.*

# VEGETABLE SPONGE

*See Loofah.*

# VINEGAR

## Herbal Vinegar

Herbal vinegars have been used for centuries as additions to bath water and as a beauty tonic. However, they can also be used to relieve headaches and to soothe a throbbing temple after exposure to the sun.

*1½ cups (150 g) fresh flower petals or herbs*
*2 cups (500 ml) cider vinegar or wine vinegar*

Put the flowers or herbs into a wide-mouthed jar. Gently warm the vinegar, pour it into the jar, seal it tightly and leave it where it will receive plenty of hot sunlight for 2 weeks. Make sure you shake the contents every day. Strain the vinegar and store it in an airtight bottle.

If the scent is not strong enough, repeat the process with a fresh batch of flower petals or herbs.

### VINEGAR FROM HERB SEEDS

Bruise the seeds with a pestle and mortar and allow 2 tablespoons of seed to every 4 cups (1 litre) of vinegar. Then prepare as for basic recipe.

Use vinegar in the following ways:

## Headache Cure

*½ cup (125 ml) lavender vinegar*
*1 cup (250 ml) rosewater (from the chemist)*

Blend the 2 ingredients thoroughly and store in an airtight bottle.

Whenever headache persists from stress or strain, dampen a handkerchief with the vinegar and lay it across your forehead for 5 to 10 minutes.

## SUN EXPOSURE

After exposure to the hot sun, dab lavender, rose or lemon verbena vinegar behind the ears and on the temples and forehead.

## WHITE VINEGAR

*See Bathroom, Brass.*
*See also First Aid.*

***Did you know ...***

that for many centuries aromatic vinegars were used to ward off infection? Doctors in the Stuart times in England carried special walking sticks with a silver knob on the end, inside which was a vinaigrette made of moss soaked in an aromatic vinegar. With this under his nose the doctor believed he would avoid being infected by his patients.

## VINYL

*See Floors, Wallpaper.*

## VIOLETS (*VIOLA ODORATA*)

Violets are delightful plants to grow in an informal garden where they are permitted to grow freely and multiply under a tree or spill over a rocky bank. They love a good, loamy soil, enriched with plenty of dark humus or compost. Once established, violets need little attention, flowering abundantly twice a year.

Made into a syrup, this herb is an excellent cough mixture for children. It is a soothing expectorant with quite a pleasant taste.

### Violet Cough Syrup

*125 g violet flowers*
*2 cups (500 ml) boiling water*
*juice of 1 large lemon*
*500 g honey*

Put the flower petals in a ceramic bowl, add the boiling

water, cover and steep for 24 hours. Strain through muslin into an enamel pan, add lemon juice and honey, bring to the boil, then reduce to a simmer until the mixture becomes thick and syrupy. Adjust if necessary by adding a little more honey.

Pour into sterilised glass jars, allow to cool and refrigerate. Take 1 teaspoon when needed.

## VOMITING

*See Pets (Vomiting).*

# WALLPAPER

Grease spots can be removed by rubbing gently with a piece of stale bread, slicing off the edge as it gets dirty. Be careful not to damage the paper and use only light pressure.

Fabric wall coverings can be cleaned by dabbing with a paste of whiting. Leave for an hour or so, then gently brush off.

Vinyl wallpaper can be cleaned with a warm cloth wrung out in vinegar.

# WATER

## GREY WATER

Grey water (water from baths and washing machines) can be siphoned off into a tank for watering vegetables and ornamentals, provided that you have used pure soap or biodegradable washing products.

## PURIFYING WATER

If you're a city dweller and conserve water by collecting it in a rainwater tank, you must purify it before you use it for drinking and cooking.

Strain the water if necessary through several layers of clean muslin cloth, then boil it for 10 minutes to destroy the germs. Allow to cool, then add a pinch of salt to each litre of water to improve its taste.

Boiled water should be used within 24 hours. To restore some of the oxygen lost through boiling, pour the water from one clean container to another several times.

Contaminated water can be purified by adding 20 drops of tincture of iodine to each litre. For cloudy water add 40 drops tincture of iodine to each litre.

*See also Garden (Water Conservation), Laundry (Softening Water).*

# WAX

To remove wax from a garment, allow it to harden, scrape off as much as possible, and then remove the rest with methylated spirits.

## WEEDS

Provided weeds and grasses are shallow-rooted, they can be eliminated from garden beds, between pavers, and so on, with a safe, natural herbicide made from human urine.

After collecting the urine allow it to stand in a covered bucket for 24 hours or more before using. Apply using a pump-spray bottle to the leaves and base of weeds.

## WEEVILS

*See Food (Moths and Weevils).*

## WINDOWS

This window and glass cleaner will not only leave your windows and mirrors sparkling clean, but will also help to keep flies out when used on external windows and glass doors.

### Lavender Glass Cleaner

*3 teaspoons dried lavender*
*2 cups (500 ml) boiling water*
*12 drops lavender oil*
*2 teaspoons methylated spirits*

Place the lavender in a bowl, add the boiling water, cover, steep overnight, then strain through muslin.

Dissolve the lavender oil in the methylated spirits, then blend it with the lavender water and drip it through filter paper. Store the cleaner in a pump-spray bottle.

Apply the cleaner with a damp cloth, then buff it off with wads of clean newspaper.

*See also Recycling (Newspapers).*

## WINE

For wine stains on garments, cover immediately with salt, and rinse in cold water before washing.

On carpets, pour a little mineral water on the stain immediately, leave for a few minutes, then blot up with a clean towel.

## WOOD BETONY

*Did you know ...*
that wood betony leaf tea is not only a good general tonic, but also an excellent substitute for conventional tea — it resembles the taste but is caffeine-free?

## WOOD STAIN

*See Timber Stain.*

## WOOLLENS

*See Laundry.*

## WORMS (GARDEN)

*See Earthworms.*

## WORMS (INTESTINAL)

*See Pets (Worms).*

## XMAS

Nowadays, with plastic Christmas trees and decorations, those typical 'Christmassy' smells of pine resin and decorative sweets no longer permeate the air. Now you can recapture that evocative aroma of Christmas with nature's essential oils. Simply spray the tree with a fragrant oil mixture, such as pine oil and water, or sprinkle a few drops of the same oil around the base of the tree. A few drops of oil on a piece of absorbent material wrapped around the bottom of the trunk is also effective.

### Christmas Tree Spray

*2 ml essential oil of pine*
*10 ml methylated spirits*
*2 cups (500 ml) distilled water*

Dissolve pine oil in methylated spirits, and add this to a pump-spray bottle containing distilled water.

### Christmas House Spray

Spray this liberally throughout the house to give it a fresh-smelling 'Christmassy' aroma. An ideal choice to make guests feel welcome and at home.

*8 drops mandarin oil*
*4 drops tangerine oil*
*2 drops cinnamon oil*
*10 ml methylated spirits*
*2 cups (500 ml) distilled water*

Dissolve the oils in the methylated spirits and add this to a pump-spray bottle containing the distilled water.

If you would like to give your spray a 'spiritual edge', include 2 drops of frankincense in the blend.

### BURNING OILS

Ceramic simmering pots are another way to fill the air with festive aromas. They are available from most herb, craft and gift shops and are usually placed on a dining table or in the lounge room.

## Christmas Oil Blend

*4 drops mandarin oil*
*1 drop geranium oil*
*1 drop cinnamon oil*
*1 cup (250 ml) boiling water*

Mix the essential oils together and add about 10 drops to the boiling water. Preheat the saucer with the candle burning, and then three-quarters fill it with the fragrant water, topping up as required.

### SCENTED WRAPPING PAPER

To make your gifts an aromatic delight, place 2 drops of essential oil on a cottonwool ball and leave it in a sealed bag with the wrapping paper overnight. You can even use different fragrances for different members of the family. Try cedarwood or frankincense for a strong smell, cinnamon or rose for sweet smells, and mandarin, a gentle smell for children, or experiment with your own choice of oils.

## YARROW (*ACHILLEA MILLEFOLIUM*)

Yarrow is an ideal plant to grow. It is easy to cultivate, and if anything, can be a bit of a problem to keep under control. But it is a beautifully flowering herb and well worth the effort.

As a companion plant, yarrow is extremely beneficial as its root excretions give vigour and strength to plants growing nearby, improving their flavour and fragrance and increasing their aromatic qualities. It makes a good neighbour in the vegetable patch, helping plants to resist disease, and to repel flies, ants and other insects.

Yarrow is an astringent and cleansing herb as well as being a styptic (a substance that will stop bleeding). Use it in face masks, face scrubs, toners for large pores and overactive sebaceous glands, shampoos and mouthwashes. However, don't use it on the face by itself as a general wash or lotion as it may cause sensitivity to sunlight.

### Yarrow Bath Lotion

Add this lotion to bath water for a relaxing, tonic bath or use it as a hair wash to dry oily hair.

*2 tablespoons yarrow flowers*
*1 teaspoon dried chamomile*
*½ cup (125 ml) boiling water*

Put herbs in a ceramic bowl, add boiling water, cover and infuse until cold. Strain through muslin and add to warm bath water, or use as a final rinse when washing your hair, massaging well into the scalp.

### Did you know ...

that yarrow leaves were used as an 'olde-worlde' love charm for those who slept alone or were contemplating a new partner?

Yarrow leaves were placed in the pillow just before going to sleep and the following verse recited:

*'Thou pretty herb of Venus' tree*
*Thy true name is Yarrow*

*Now who my bosom friend must be*
*Pray tell thou me tomorrow.*

Prior to awakening next morning, a vision of a future husband, wife, lover or bosom friend would be seen.

## YEAST

This recipe for making your own yeast starter, to use when baking bread, was found among the yellowing pages of my grandmother's handwritten recipes and formulas. I have used this recipe now for more than 15 years and found it to be extremely successful.

### Yeast Starter

*1 potato*
*1 tablespoon hops*
*1 tablespoon sugar*
*1 tablespoon plain (all-purpose) flour*
*2 raisins*

Wash the potato and quarter it — do not peel it. Cook it in a saucepan with hops. Pour off the water and reserve it, then mash the potato and hops with sugar and flour. Mix with the reserved water and put in a glass jar with raisins. Seal tightly and leave in a warm place to ferment.

Keep back some of the liquid yeast to start the next culture when you are baking.

## YLANG YLANG

The beautiful yellow flower of the ylang ylang tree has an exotic scent somewhat similar to a mixture of jasmine and almond blossom. Its pleasant-smelling oil is said to soothe anger and frustration, revitalise the body and calm, comfort and satisfy the nerves. This exotic oil is also considered to have aphrodisiac qualities and is believed to be helpful in overcoming impotence and frigidity.

Ylang ylang oil is good to use in facial massages, and is particularly good for oily skin. It is often used in perfumes and included in bath oils and room freshener sprays.

## REVITALISATION BATH

Revitalise yourself after a busy day, when you still have to go out in the evening, by adding a few drops of ylang ylang oil and bergamot oil to a warmish bath and soak in it for 10 minutes.

## SPECIAL OCCASION BATH

For a special occasion, when you want to feel particularly good, enjoy a soaking bath or a massage of the following blend: equal quantities of ylang ylang, sandalwood and rose.

Add 2 drops each of the oils to a warmish bath, or 2 drops each to 20 ml of grapeseed oil for a full body massage.

## Z IS FOR ZEALOUS
## AND QUITE ZANY.

If you have read this far this book has, I hope, sparked off an insatiable desire and interest in the versatile use of herbs, and other natural substances, for making environmentally safe products that deal with many daily situations in and around the home.

You will discover how zealous you must be to work in harmony with Nature, and how zany you will appear to the unconverted. But carry on regardless, as you discover the cumulative benefits that Nature has to offer, for both your health and that of the environment.

## A NOTE ABOUT MEASUREMENTS

Liquid measurements that are small are given in teaspoons and tablespoons, where 1 teaspoon = 5 ml, 1 tablespoon = 20 ml. It is very important that you do not use metal spoons when measuring essential oils; they may be affected by the metal. It is best to use droppers for very small quantities as this allows greater accuracy, and plastic spoons and glass jugs for larger quantities.

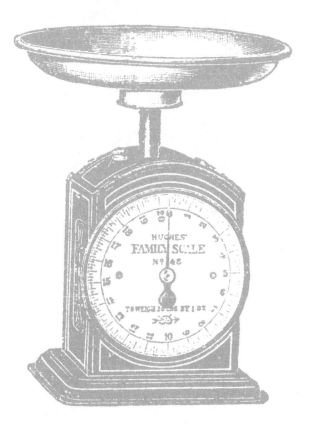